CRAFTSMAN

& Other Timeless American Dream Homes

DESIGNSDIRECT PUBLISHING

PRESIDENT Angela Santerini

PUBLISHER Dominic Foley

EDITOR Darlene Fuhst

WRITER Jennifer Bacon

GRAPHIC ARTIST Bishana Shipp

CONTRIBUTING EDITORS
Shannon Addis
Jennifer Baker
Laura Segers
Heidi Haunold

CONTRIBUTING GRAPHIC ARTISTS
Kim Campeau
Emily Sessa
Joshua Thomas
Diane Zwack

CONTRIBUTING WRITERS
Claire Ulik
Laura Segers
Sara Hockman
Jeffrey deRoulet

ILLUSTRATORS
Architectural Art
Allen Bennetts
Anita Bice
Rod Dent
Greg Havens
Holzhauer, Inc.
Dave Jenkins
Kurt Kauss
Miles Milton
Barry Nathan

PHOTOGRAPHERS
Walter Kirk
Matthew Scott
Laurence Taylor
Happy Terrebone
Doug Thompson
Bryan Willy
CJ Walker

A Designs Direct Publishing® Book
Printed by Toppan Printing Co., Hong Kong
First Printing, February 2007

10 9 8 7 6 5 4 3 2 1

ISBN softcover:
(10-digit) 1-932553-23-1
(13-digit) 978-1-932553-23-9

CRAFTSMAN AND OTHER TIMELESS AMERICAN DREAM HOMES is a book of immaculately designed homes that exemplify true Craftsman style, as well as plans that showcase traces of the Victorian and Arts and Crafts movements. To better appreciate these styles one must understand the history behind the Craftsman movement, as it was a time of true innovation in not only architecture, but lifestyles as well.

When most hear the word Craftsman, they typically think "bungalow" or homes that refer to an earlier time. While it's true that the Craftsman style does include homes that were originally one-and-a-half stories with low-slung roofs, low to the ground and included arched-interior openings, it is more accurately a subset of the massive Arts and Crafts movement of the early 1900s. Begun as a reaction against the Industrial Revolution, the Arts and Crafts movement rebelled against mass-produced technology and focused on creativity and the human touch. It aimed to create new and beautiful environments for people to live in, complete with fine craftsmanship and attractive building materials.

As the Arts and Crafts movement spread across Europe and into America, it accrued several styles and leaders, including William Morris and Gustav Stickley. Morris--a poet and artist, is often considered the founder of the movement and advocated functional art and architecture. His appreciation for simplicity and quality in craftsmanship typically focused on the use of natural materials. This was in stark contrast to the ornate architecture of the previous Victorian Movement. Widely popular and very formal, Victorian architecture is best known for its use of turrets, gothic and medieval features, wraparound porches and fanciful details. Although homes of the Victorian period are gorgeous by design, Morris sought to simplify the architecture of the era.

U.S. furniture designer Gustav Stickley was also one of the first influential proponents of the movement. His magazine, *The Craftsman*, was published from 1900-1916 and published plans for Arts and Crafts-style homes. These plans became known as Craftsman homes and were popular across the U.S. from the 1900s to the 1930s. Commonly named the Craftsman Bungalow, these classic homes typically feature wide, overhanging eaves, low-pitched roofs, porches with square columns and interior traits of built-in cabinets, shelves and seating.

Some 100 years after taking the world by storm, Craftsman homes are still as popular as they were in the early 1900s. It is in this collection that you will find homes that Stickley and Morris inspired. These modern plans still possess the same traits of the bungalows from years ago, including large outdoor living spaces, interior built-ins, natural materials such as wood and stone for exteriors, shed dormers and deep porches. The homes in this collection bring the popular Craftsman look back to life.

While Craftsman homes celebrate the simple structure of a home, the homes featured in the coming pages emulate that style of simplicity yet include a touch of modern flair. After all, making life easier through open floor plans and efficient space utilization was originally the Craftsman way.

...large outdoor living spaces, interior built-ins, natural materials such as wood and stone for exteriors, shed dormers and deep porches,...

refined craftsman `4`

rustic craftsman `60`

timeless american `118`

REFINED CRAFTSMAN

The Ventura; See page 52

At home in any suburb or streetscape, these REFINED CRAFTSMAN homes exhibit traditional Craftsman elements. Step back in time with classic-looking facades filled with deep porches, square columns, oversized shed dormers and low-hanging eaves. Modern conveniences enhance the layouts and perfectly blend a hint of nostalgia with the amenities today's families need. If you're searching for a traditional Craftsman home, look no further.

© 2003 Frank Betz Associates, Inc.

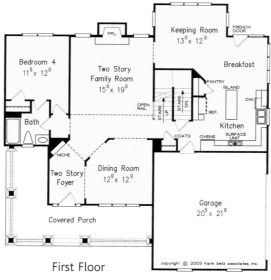

First Floor

Keeping Room
13⁰ x 12⁰

FPL.

FRENCH DOOR

Bedroom 4
11⁵ x 12⁰

Two Story Family Room
15⁰ x 19⁰

Breakfast

PANTRY

ISLAND

OPEN RAIL

Bath

STAIRS UP   STAIRS DN

DW.

REF.

Kitchen

COATS

OVENS

SURFACE UNIT

NICHE

SURFACE UNIT

Two Story Foyer

Dining Room
12⁰ x 12⁰

Garage
20⁵ x 21⁹

Covered Porch

copyright © 2003 frank betz associates, inc.

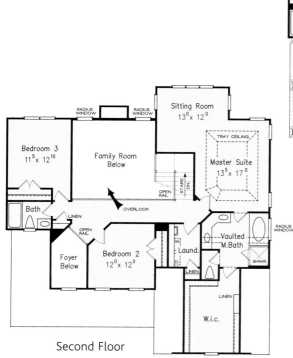

Second Floor

Sitting Room
13⁰ x 12⁰

RADIUS WINDOW   RADIUS WINDOW

TRAY CEILING

Bedroom 3
11⁵ x 12¹⁰

Family Room Below

Master Suite
13⁵ x 17⁰

OPEN RAIL   STAIRS DN

Bath

LINEN

OVERLOOK

OPEN RAIL

RADIUS WINDOW

Vaulted M.Bath

Foyer Below

Bedroom 2
12⁰ x 12⁰

W.   Laund.

D.

LINEN

SHWR.

LINEN

W.i.c.

The Craftsman-style home has made a comeback! Tapered columns and Mission-styled windows, combined with earthen stone and cedar shakes, make the *Bakersfield* reminiscent of the Craftsman era. Relaxing family time is well-spent in the keeping room just off the kitchen. Tray ceilings and a private lounging area make the master suite a true retreat.

Bakersfield

Frank Betz Associates, Inc.

CHPFB01-3783
1-888-840-6020

Bedrooms:	4
Bath:	3
Width:	48'0"
Depth:	50'0"
1st Floor:	1322 sq ft
2nd Floor:	1262 sq ft
Living Area:	2584 sq ft
Foundation:	Slab, Crawl Space or Basement
Price Code:	H

Rear Elevation

A portico impresses with an arch and stately columns. Inside, charm merges with a family-efficient floor plan. The kitchen partitions the dining room and breakfast area, easily accessing a screened porch for outdoor entertaining. A tray ceiling crowns the master bedroom, while a curved balcony separates additional bedrooms.

Rockledge
Donald A. Gardner Architects, Inc.
CHPDG01-875-D
1-888-840-6020

Bedrooms:	4
Bath:	3-1/2
Width:	79'0"
Depth:	68'2"
1st Floor:	1682 sq ft
2nd Floor:	577 sq ft
Basement Floor:	690 sq ft
Total Living:	2949 sq ft
Bonus Room:	459 sq ft
Foundation:	Hillside Walkout
Price Code:	F

Rear Elevation

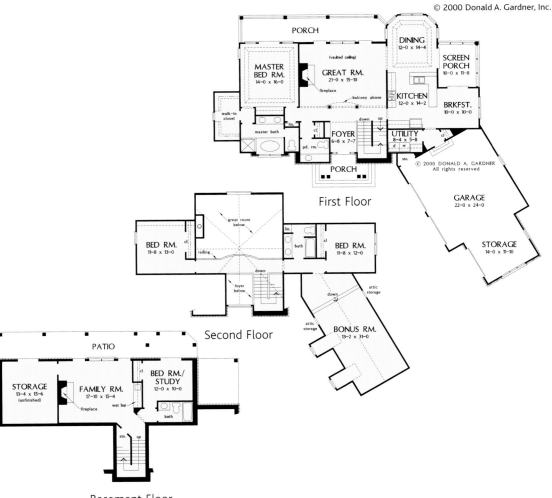

© 2000 Donald A. Gardner, Inc.

First Floor

Second Floor

Basement Floor

© CornerStone Designs, LLC.

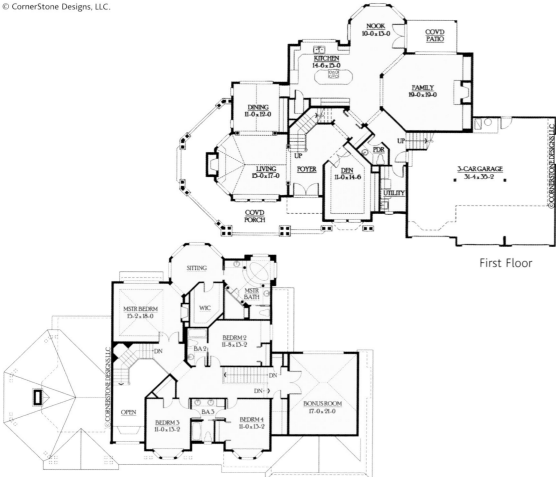

First Floor

Second Floor

This grand Craftsman estate creates a feeling of elegance while providing every modern convenience. The floor plan marries vaulted formal rooms and open family spaces to the outdoors with generous front and rear covered porches. A grand front stair leads to the luxurious master suite, while the private back stair accesses the bonus room and three secondary bedrooms.

Cedar Grove
CornerStone Designs
CHPCD01-M4100A3F-0
1-888-840-6020

Bedrooms:	4
Bath:	3-1/2
Width:	90'0"
Depth:	60'0"
1st Floor:	2075 sq ft
2nd Floor:	2145 sq ft
Living Area:	4220 sq ft
Foundation:	Crawl Space
Price Code:	H

Rear Elevation

ABBOTTS POND
frank betz associates, inc.

This cozy charmer exudes warmth from the moment it comes into view, with an inviting entrance that encourages friends and family to come inside. Thoughtfully placed windows and French doors usher light into the home, blurring the line between inside and outside. The kitchen is spacious enough for two chefs, and features a step-saving layout, large pantry and a convenient pass-through for serving in the dining and great rooms. The master bedroom boasts a two-tiered tray ceiling and access to the adjoining bath through an elegant French door. Completing the master suite, a large walk-in closet includes dedicated linen space.

Above:
The vaulted family room features a fireplace that serves as an elegant focal point.
Right:
Looking over the rear porch and accented by a vaulted ceiling, the dining room is the perfect formal room for entertaining.

Craftsman's Corner

Arched entryways in the interior and divided upper-window sashes bring this Craftsman home to life.

Above Left and Right:
The kitchen pass-through and arched entryway enhance the open feel while creating a transition from the family room to the kitchen.

Right:
Dark furniture and light walls and carpet create the perfect blend in this spacious master.

Exterior:
(Front) Tapered columns give this Craftsman bungalow a charming façade sure to accent any streetscape.

© 2003 Frank Betz Associates, Inc.

Rear Elevation

Frank Betz Associates, Inc.

CHPFB01-3856
1-888-840-6020

Bedrooms:	3
Bath:	2
Width:	50'4"
Depth:	49'0"
1st Floor:	1406 sq ft
Living Area:	1406 sq ft
Foundation:	Slab, Crawl Space or Basement
Price Code:	E

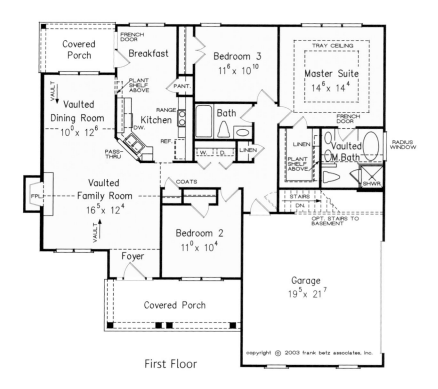

First Floor

© The Sater Design Collection, Inc.

A column-lined entry porch leads through double doors to a broad foyer. The open floor plan is perfect for entertaining. The great room boasts a built-in entertainment center, coffered ceiling, a double-sided fireplace and French doors to the rear porch. The step-saver kitchen has a unique diamond shape. The master bedroom boasts a bayed window, French doors to the rear porch and a luxurious bath.

Madison

The Sater Design Collection, Inc.

CHPDS01-7064
1-888-840-6020

Bedrooms:	3
Bath:	2
Width:	80'6"
Depth:	66'0"
1st Floor:	2454 sq ft
Living Area:	2454 sq ft
Bonus Room:	256 sq ft
Foundation:	Crawl Space
Price Code:	F

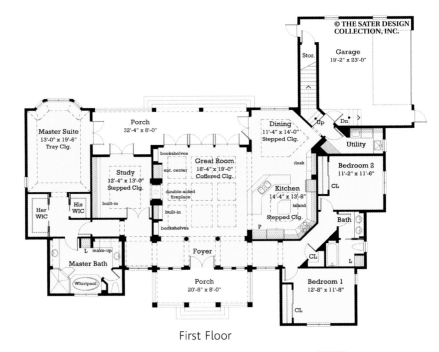

First Floor

Second Floor

Rear Elevation

© 2005 Frank Betz Associates, Inc.

First Floor

Second Floor

The brick front porch and columns of the *Capistrano* are the perfect backdrop for a tranquil spot to end the day. The arrangement of the kitchen and keeping room make entertaining a breeze. The second floor houses three additional bedrooms and an optional bonus room.

Capistrano
Frank Betz Associates, Inc.
CHPFB01-3920
1-888-840-6020

Bedrooms:	4
Bath:	3-1/2
Width:	56'0"
Depth:	53'4"
1st Floor:	1919 sq ft
2nd Floor:	876 sq ft
Living Area:	2795 sq ft
Bonus Room:	167 sq ft
Foundation:	Slab, Crawl Space or Basement
Price Code:	I

Rear Elevation

© 1999 Donald A. Gardner, Inc.

Cedar shake and siding lend warmth and style to this Craftsman home with finished basement. A cathedral ceiling spans the open great room and spacious, center island kitchen for exceptional volume. A deep tray ceiling heightens the dining room, while a vaulted ceiling enhances the breakfast room. Two rear decks and a screened porch augment the home's ample living space.

Clairemont

Donald A. Gardner Architects, Inc.
CHPDG01-791-D
1-888-840-6020

Bedrooms:	4
Bath:	3
Width:	83'0"
Depth:	74'4"
1st Floor:	2122 sq ft
Basement Floor:	1150 sq ft
Total Living:	3272 sq ft
Foundation:	Hillside Walkout
Price Code:	G

First Floor

© 1999 DONALD A. GARDNER
All rights reserved

Basement Floor

Rear Elevation

© CornerStone Designs, LLC.

First Floor

FAMILY
13-6 x 15-6

NOOK
10-8 x 11-6

KITCHEN
12-6 x 13-6

UTILITY

UP

PDR

DINING
11-0 x 12-4

2-CAR GARAGE
19-0 x 19-2

LIVING
12-4 x 15-6

FOYER

ENTRY

© CORNERSTONE DESIGNS LLC

First Floor

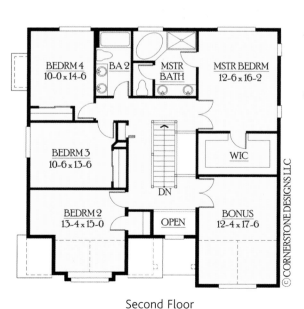

BEDRM 4
10-0 x 14-6

BA 2

MSTR
BATH

MSTR BEDRM
12-6 x 16-2

BEDRM 3
10-6 x 13-6

WIC

DN

BEDRM 2
13-4 x 15-0

OPEN

BONUS
12-4 x 17-6

© CORNERSTONE DESIGNS LLC

Second Floor

Classic details distinguish this amazingly compact and versatile home. The exterior is accented with shingles, arches, oval and bay windows, while the floor plan flows easily through spacious formal and family living spaces. The spacious master suite is segregated from the children for welcome privacy, while the generous bonus room is a perfect spot for TV and games.

Greenwood

CornerStone Designs

CHPCD01-M2590D2F-0
1-888-840-6020

Bedrooms:	4
Bath:	2-1/2
Width:	42'0"
Depth:	42'0"
1st Floor:	1190 sq ft
2nd Floor:	1461 sq ft
Living Area:	2651 sq ft
Foundation:	Crawl Space
Price Code:	F

Rear Elevation

WHITEHEART

donald a. gardner architects, inc.

From metal and shingles to cedar shake and stone, this soon-to-be favorite blends with a variety of settings and adds a touch of timelessness to any streetscape or lot.

Greeting with columns, sidelights and a transom, the front entry leads to an open interior. Columns and decorative ceilings define common rooms without enclosing them. The great room features a vaulted ceiling, fireplace and built-ins, while the kitchen includes a serviceable pass-through. A bay window extends the breakfast area, and the master bedroom's tray ceiling is arched to accommodate the top of a circlehead window transom.

Above Right:
The center island is an excellent gathering space in this kitchen filled with ample counter space and cabinetry.

Right: A towering stone fireplace and clerestory draw the eye upwards in the great room.

Exteriors:
(Front) Prominent gable peaks lend drama to this exterior comprised of brick and shake for immediate curb appeal.
(Rear) Porches and patios provide entertaining space aplenty in the rear exterior.

Rear Elevation

DONALD A. GARDNER ARCHITECTS, INC.
CHPDG01-926
1-888-840-6020

Bedrooms: 3
Bath: 2
Width: 57'8"
Depth: 64'4"
1st Floor: 2252 sq ft
Living Area: 2252 sq ft
Foundation: Crawl Space*
Price Code: E

*Other options available. See page 175.

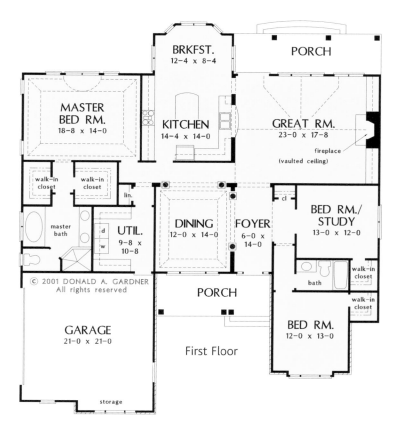

MASTER BED RM.
18-8 x 14-0

walk-in closet

walk-in closet

lin.

master bath

UTIL.
9-8 x 10-8

d w

BRKFST.
12-4 x 8-4

KITCHEN
14-4 x 14-0

DINING
12-0 x 14-0

FOYER
6-0 x 14-0

PORCH

GREAT RM.
23-0 x 17-8

fireplace
(vaulted ceiling)

cl

BED RM./ STUDY
13-0 x 12-0

bath

walk-in closet

walk-in closet

GARAGE
21-0 x 21-0

PORCH

BED RM.
12-0 x 13-0

First Floor

storage

The *Kensington Park's* kitchen, breakfast area and family room are all open to each other creating easy access from one area to the next. A butler's pantry connects the kitchen to the dining room for convenient entertaining. A mudroom just off the garage is equipped with a bench, wall hooks, a broom closet and access to the laundry room.

Kensington Park

Frank Betz Associates, Inc.

CHPFB01-3910
1-888-840-6020

Bedrooms:	4
Bath:	3-1/2
Width:	56'0"
Depth:	53'0"
1st Floor:	1755 sq ft
2nd Floor:	864 sq ft
Living Area:	2619 sq ft
Foundation:	Slab, Crawl Space or Basement
Price Code:	G

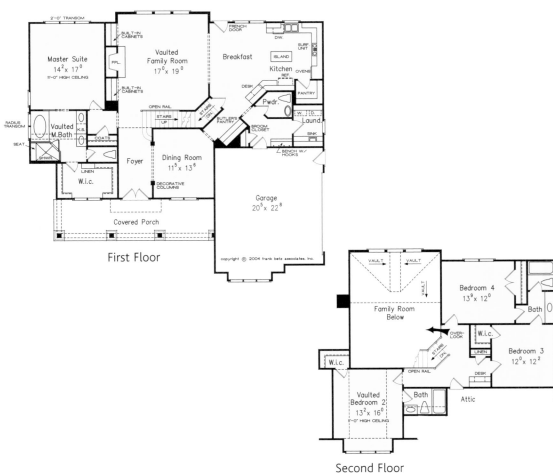

First Floor

Second Floor

Rear Elevation

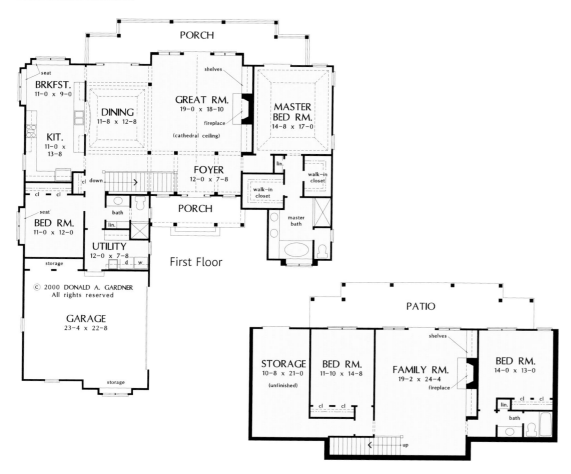

First Floor

Basement Floor

Designed with a partial, finished walkout basement, this hillside home boasts a number of custom details. Tray ceilings enhance the dining room and master bedroom, while box-bay windows brighten the breakfast area and first-floor secondary bedroom. Secluded for privacy, the master suite features his and her walk-in closets, a linen closet and luxurious bath.

Glen Haven

Donald A. Gardner Architects, Inc.
CHPDG01-843-D
1-888-840-6020

Bedrooms:	4
Bath:	3
Width:	59'4"
Depth:	73'2"
1st Floor:	2000 sq ft
Basement Floor:	1104 sq ft
Total Living:	3104 sq ft
Foundation:	Hillside Walkout
Price Code:	G

Rear Elevation

© CornerStone Designs, LLC.

A seamless transition between indoors and outdoors is the hallmark of this charmer. Easy living flows through the generous island kitchen, spacious nook and vaulted great room with its dramatic see-through gas fireplace out to the grand covered rear patio. The bold façade features columns and brackets with classic board and batten, shingle and stone accents.

Stoneridge

CornerStone Designs
CHPCD01-R1725A3FT-0
1-888-840-6020

Bedrooms:	2
Bath:	2
Width:	64'0"
Depth:	53'6"
1st Floor:	1725 sq ft
Living Area:	1725 sq ft
Foundation:	Crawl Space
Price Code:	D

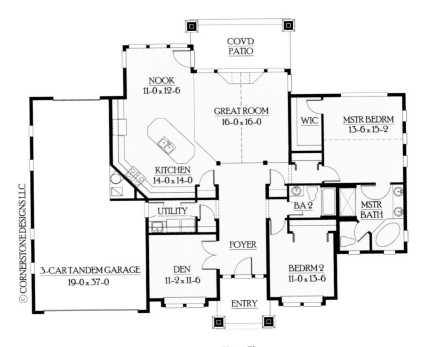

First Floor

Rear Elevation

© 2001 Donald A. Gardner, Inc.

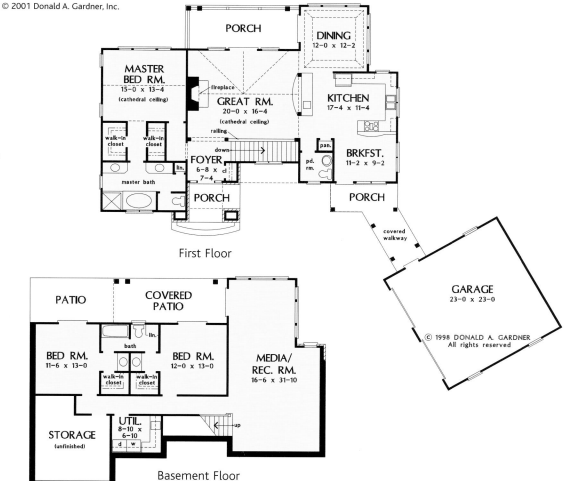

First Floor

PORCH

DINING
12-0 x 12-2

MASTER BED RM.
15-0 x 13-4
(cathedral ceiling)

fireplace

GREAT RM.
20-0 x 16-4
(cathedral ceiling)

KITCHEN
17-4 x 11-4

walk-in closet

walk-in closet

railing

FOYER
6-8 x 7-4

down

pd. rm.

pan.

BRKFST.
11-2 x 9-2

lin.

cl.

master bath

PORCH

PORCH

covered walkway

GARAGE
23-0 x 23-0

Basement Floor

PATIO

COVERED PATIO

BED RM.
11-6 x 13-0

bath

BED RM.
12-0 x 13-0

MEDIA/ REC. RM.
16-6 x 31-10

walk-in closet

walk-in closet

lin.

STORAGE
(unfinished)

UTIL.
8-10 x 6-10

d   w

up

Designed for sloping lots, this stone and stucco home takes advantage of rear views. The floor plan features an open design with cathedral ceilings in the great room and master bedroom and a tray ceiling in the dining room. A wet bar is situated between the kitchen and great room, and the back porch is accessible from the dining room and great room.

Sable Ridge

Donald A. Gardner Architects, Inc.
CHPDG01-710-D
1-888-840-6020

Bedrooms:	3
Bath:	2-1/2
Width:	53'8"
Depth:	40'4"
1st Floor:	1472 sq ft
Basement Floor:	1211 sq ft
Total Living:	2683 sq ft
Foundation:	Hillside Walkout
Price Code:	F

Rear Elevation

BEGONIA
cornerstone designs, llc

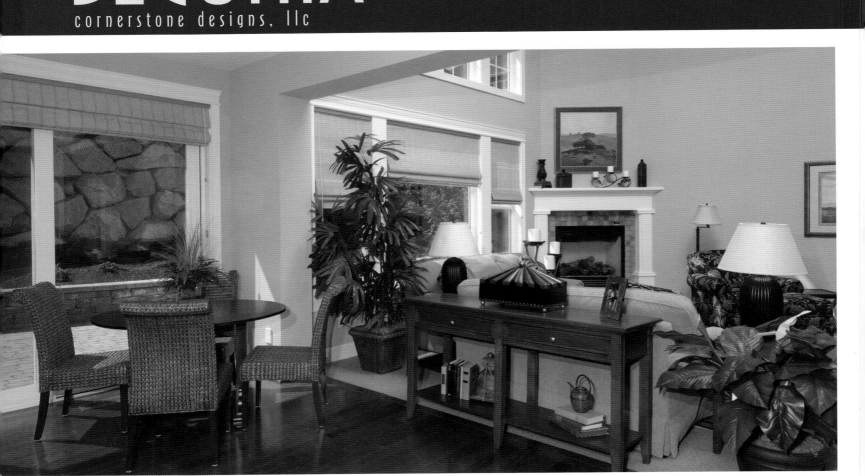

Hampton-style elegance meets country charm in this compact classic. Traditional dormers, corbels and bays accent the inviting façade. The dramatic circular stair rotunda with its curving second-story hallway is truly the heart of the home.

The innovative floor plan is organized around a strong diagonal axis leading from the entry to the family room hearth. A romantic "Romeo & Juliet" balcony overlooks the volume family room, highlighting a generous informal living zone at the rear. The octagonal foyer gives access to the formal zone, the den opposite the living and dining rooms, all distinguished with coffered ceilings.

The upstairs master suite features a fireplace and soaking tub. An open play loft connects two children's bedrooms, while a fourth bedroom, a convenient laundry and large bonus room round out the upper floor.

Above:
The cozy breakfast nook opens into the grand volume of the two-story family room. Dark-stained hardwood floors and taupe wall surfaces contrast with painted white trim and casework details

Right:
The spectacular circular stair rotunda provides everyday charm and delight while making a wonderful backdrop for seasonal decorations. The foyer is flanked by pairs of French doors leading to the den and formal living room.

Craftsman's Corner

The use of natural materials such as stone and shingles enhances this Craftsman exterior.

Above:
The gourmet kitchen's dark-stained cabinets combine with black granite countertops, tile backsplashes and stainless-steel appliances to create a luxurious atmosphere.

Right:
Traditional painted casings, wainscots, and stepped ceilings highlighted by crown moldings accent the spaces.

Exteriors:
(Front) The entry porch is a traditional touch, while projecting bay windows and bold, contrasting trim create a fresh, elegant Craftsman look.
(Rear) An abundance of glass brings maximum natural light deep into the interior, while providing broad views of the surrounding landscape.

Rear Elevation

CornerStone Designs, LLC

CHPCD01-M3555A3FT-0
1-888-840-6020

Bedrooms:	4
Bath:	2-1/2
Width:	50'0"
Depth:	58'0"
1st Floor:	1629 sq ft
2nd Floor:	1926 sq ft
Living Area:	3555 sq ft
Foundation:	Crawl Space*
Price Code:	G

© CornerStone Designs, LLC

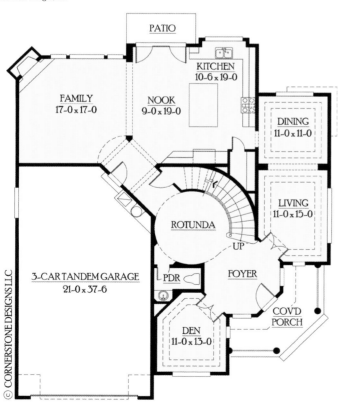

First Floor

PATIO

KITCHEN
10-6 x 19-0

FAMILY
17-0 x 17-0

NOOK
9-0 x 19-0

DINING
11-0 x 11-0

LIVING
11-0 x 15-0

ROTUNDA

UP

3-CAR TANDEM GARAGE
21-0 x 37-6

PDR

FOYER

COV'D PORCH

DEN
11-0 x 13-0

© CORNERSTONE DESIGNS LLC

Second Floor

OPEN

MSTR BEDRM
13-2 x 20-0

WIC

MSTR BATH

BEDRM 2
11-8 x 13-0

UTILITY

DN

OPEN

BEDRM 4
11-2 x 15-6

BA 2

UP

LOFT
10-0 x 10-0

BONUS
17-0 x 17-0

BEDRM 3
11-0 x 13-2

© CORNERSTONE DESIGNS LLC

refined craftsman

This design creates a lasting impression, from the exterior to the interior. Elegant columns are used to give distinction to the covered breezeway and formal dining room. The great room features a two-story vaulted ceiling, built-ins and French doors. The breakfast area is extended by a bay window.

Greystone

Donald A. Gardner Architects, Inc.
CHPDG01-919
1-888-840-6020

Bedrooms:	4
Bath:	2-1/2
Width:	50'0"
Depth:	71'8"
1st Floor:	1707 sq ft
2nd Floor:	514 sq ft
Total Living:	2221 sq ft
Bonus Room:	211 sq ft
Foundation:	Crawl Space*
Price Code:	E

*Other options available. See page 175.

Rear Elevation

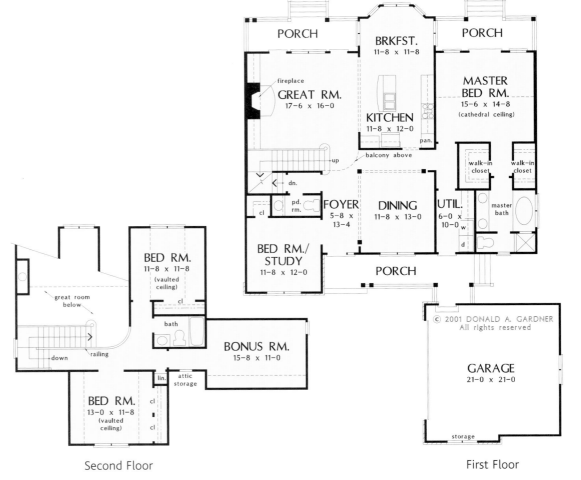

Second Floor

First Floor

© 2005 Frank Betz Associates, Inc.

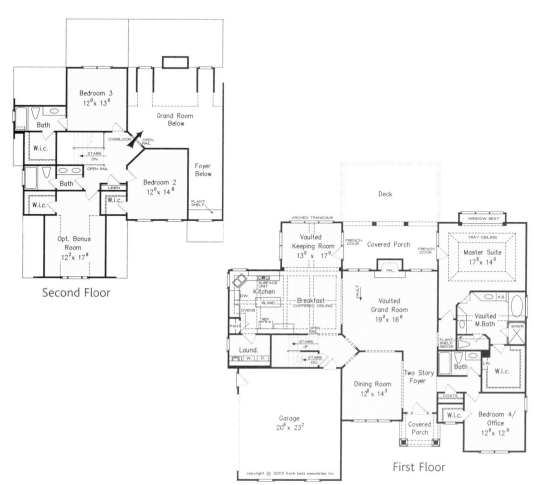

Second Floor

First Floor

The *Palisades* welcomes its homeowners with its Craftsman style. A vaulted family room flanks the fireplace with windows that allow views to the backyard as well as let in the natural light. A keeping room is the perfect place for the family to unwind at the end of the day. The breakfast and kitchen area are highlightd by the coffered ceiling.

Palisades
Frank Betz Associates, Inc.
CHPFB01-3918
1-888-840-6020

Bedrooms: 4
Bath: 4
Width: 60'0"
Depth: 56'0"
1st Floor: 2042 sq ft
2nd Floor: 647 sq ft
Living Area: 2689 sq ft
Bonus Room: 243 sq ft
Foundation: Slab, Crawl Space or Basement
Price Code: I

Rear Elevation

© The Sater Design Collection, Inc.

Repeating arches, gables and dual sets of Tuscan columns add interest to the front façade. The spacious grand room features built-in cabinetry, a cozy fireplace and French doors to the lanai. A well-crafted kitchen has wrapping counter space, a walk-in pantry and easy access to the formal dining room. A split-floor plan ensures privacy for the master suite and secondary bedrooms. The extensive lanai is accessible from the master suite, grand room, nook and a secondary bedroom.

Tucker Town Way

The Sater Design Collection, Inc.

CHPDS01-6692
1-888-840-6020

Bedrooms:	3
Bath:	2
Width:	59'8"
Depth:	54'0"
1st Floor:	2190 sq ft
Living Area:	2190 sq ft
Foundation:	Island Basement
Price Code:	F

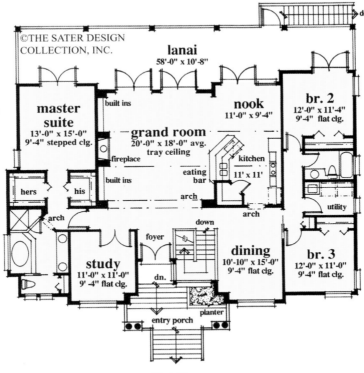

First Floor

Lower Level

Rear Elevation

© CornerStone Designs, LLC.

First Floor

BONUS
13-8 x 15-4

BEDRM 3
9-8 x 13-4

OPEN

BA 2

DN

BEDRM 2
10-0 x 11-4

WIC

MSTR BEDRM
13-4 x 15-4

MSTR BATH

DECK

© CORNERSTONE DESIGNS LLC

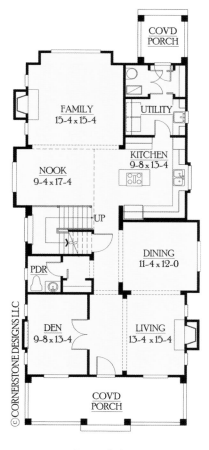

Second Floor

COVD PORCH

FAMILY
15-4 x 15-4

UTILITY

NOOK
9-4 x 17-4

KITCHEN
9-8 x 13-4

UP

DINING
11-4 x 12-0

PDR

DEN
9-8 x 13-4

LIVING
13-4 x 15-4

COVD PORCH

© CORNERSTONE DESIGNS LLC

A timeless bungalow designed for a modern lifestyle, the *Ferndale* brings country charm to the city or contemporary elegance to the country. The welcoming front porch is the perfect place to pass time or greet the neighbors. The nook and stairwell windows flood the center of the house with light. The spacious master suite is insulated from the children's bedrooms and the bonus room.

Ferndale

CornerStone Designs

CHPCD01-M2505A3RD-0
1-888-840-6020

Bedrooms: 3
Bath: 2-1/2
Width: 30'0"
Depth: 68'0"
1st Floor: 1360 sq ft
2nd Floor: 1145 sq ft
Living Area: 2505 sq ft
Foundation: Crawl Space
Price Code: F

Rear Elevation

DUNE RIDGE
the sater design collection, inc.

This home celebrates the outdoors, with a floor plan that provides smart transitions between public and private realms.

The formal dining room is an open space defined by columns and a tray ceiling. Nearby is the impressive great room, which features a fireplace, built-in cabinetry and glass doors. A convenient pass-through connects the space to the kitchen. The private master retreat boasts a stepped ceiling, double walk-in closets, access to the back porch and a lavish bath.

On the lower level, the family room is the perfect spot for entertaining. Nearby, an "in-law" kitchen prepares drinks and snacks for all to enjoy.

Above Right:
 A bright and airy breakfast nook, center work island with prep sink, plenty of storage space and a pass-through to the great room will please cooks of all levels.

Right:
 A vaulted coffered ceiling, glass doors opening to the back porch, a fireplace and built-in cabinetry add character to the spacious room.

Exteriors:
(Front) Tapered columns, ornamental trellis brackets, exposed beams in overhanging eaves and a pleasing mix of stone and cedar shake iterate the careful attention to detail that went into the design of this Craftsman inspired home.
(Rear) Multiple windows and glass doors provide a seamless connection with the outdoors while a predominant center gable brings in the sun's rays through square transoms.

© The Sater Design Collection,, Inc.

Rear Elevation

The Sater Design Collection, Inc

CHPDS01-7078

1-888-840-6020

Bedrooms:	3
Bath:	2-1/2
Width:	76'8"
Depth:	52'11"
1st Floor:	1711 sq ft
Basement:	1193 sq ft
Living Area:	2904 sq ft
Foundation:	Basement
Price Code:	O

Photographed home may have been modified from the original construction documents.

First Floor

Lower Level

© 2002 Donald A. Gardner, Inc.

Craftsman materials added to a traditional house yield incredible curb appeal. The front-entry garage makes it ideal for narrow lots. The open floor plan features a first-floor master suite, screened porch and conveniently located powder room. Upstairs, a loft overlooks the open great room and foyer, and two secondary bedrooms are positioned for privacy.

Madaridge

Donald A. Gardner Architects, Inc.

CHPDG01-974
1-888-840-6020

Bedrooms:	3
Bath:	2-1/2
Width:	40'4"
Depth:	70'0"
1st Floor:	1496 sq ft
2nd Floor:	615 sq ft
Total Living:	2111 sq ft
Bonus Room:	277 sq ft
Foundation:	Crawl Space*
Price Code:	E

*Other options available. See page 175.

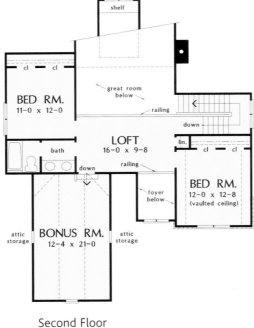

Rear Elevation

Second Floor

shelf

cl cl

BED RM.
11-0 x 12-0

great room below

railing

down

LOFT
16-0 x 9-8

bath

down

railing

lin.

cl   cl

foyer below

BED RM.
12-0 x 12-8
(vaulted ceiling)

attic storage

BONUS RM.
12-4 x 21-0

attic storage

First Floor

MASTER BED RM.
14-0 x 12-10
(vaulted ceiling)

walk-in closet

walk-in closet

SCREEN PORCH
11-4 x 13-4

PORCH

BRKFST.
11-4 x 10-4

fireplace

GREAT RM.
16-0 x 17-4
(vaulted ceiling)

cabinets

master bath

UTIL.
6-0 x 9-4

pantry

KITCHEN
10-8 x 9-8

w
d

cl

sto.

balcony above

up

pd. rm.

cabinets

FOYER
6-0 x 8-8

(two story ceiling)

DINING
12-0 x 13-0

GARAGE
21-0 x 21-0

PORCH

© 2002 Frank Betz Associates, Inc.

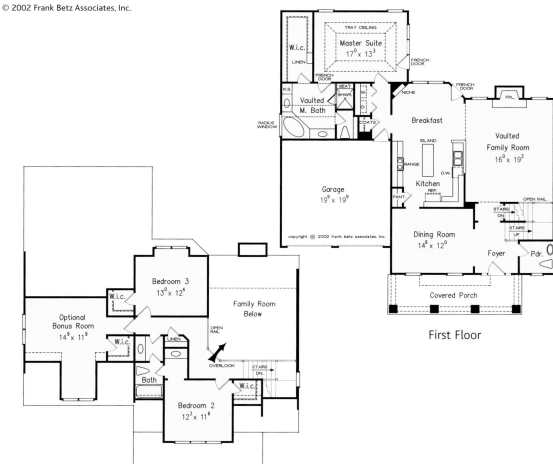

First Floor

Second Floor

C harm and character abound from the façade of the *Pasadena*. Inside, the master suite is privately tucked away on the rear of the main level. Upstairs, an optional bonus room is available that can be used as the homeowner wishes — a playroom, home office or fitness room are all fantastic options.

Pasadena
Frank Betz Associates, Inc.
CHPFB01-3756
1-888-840-6020

Bedrooms:	3
Bath:	2-1/2
Width:	50'0"
Depth:	57'0"
1st Floor:	1561 sq ft
2nd Floor:	578 sq ft
Living Area:	2139 sq ft
Bonus Room:	274 sq ft
Foundation:	Slab, Crawl Space or Basement
Price Code:	H

Rear Elevation

© The Sater Design Collection, Inc.

Decorative shutters, fretwork, gables, multi-paned windows and an inviting front porch garner attention from those who pass by. The island kitchen shares an eating bar with the great room and offers ample counter and storage space. An indulgent master suite offers a luxurious bath, dual walk-in closets, a vaulted ceiling and access to the back porch.

Whisperwood
The Sater Design Collection, Inc.
CHPDS01-6844
1-888-840-6020

Bedrooms: 3
Bath: 2
Width: 44'0"
Depth: 63'0"
1st Floor: 2137 sq ft
Living Area: 2137 sq ft
Foundation: Island Basement
Price Code: F

Rear Elevation

First Floor

Porch
29'-0" x 9'-0"
10'-0" Clg.

Master Suite
13'-0" x 16'-0"
Vaulted Clg.

Great Room
17'-0" x 17'-6"
12'-0" Hip Vaulted Clg.

Nook
10'-6" x 10'-0"
10'-0" Clg.

W.I.C.

W.I.C.

Fireplace

Built-ins

Built-ins

M. Bath

Kitchen
11'-0" x 14'-0"
10'-0" Clg.

Walk-in Shower

Whirlpool

Tub

Bath

Dn.

Dining
11'-0" x 13'-0"
11'-0" Tray Clg.

Foyer

Utility
10'-0" Clg.

Lin.

Lin.

Bedroom 2
11'-8" x 13'-0"
10'-0" Clg.

Bedroom 3
11'-8" x 13'-0"
10'-0" Clg.

Entry Porch

© THE SATER DESIGN COLLECTION, INC.

Lower Level

Covered Porch
29'-0" x 9'-0"
9'-4" Clg.

Firewood Storage

Mud Area
9'-0" Clg.

Up.

Foyer

Storage/ Bonus Room
9'-0" Clg.

2 Car Garage
9'-0" Clg.

Ski Storage

© THE SATER DESIGN COLLECTION, INC.

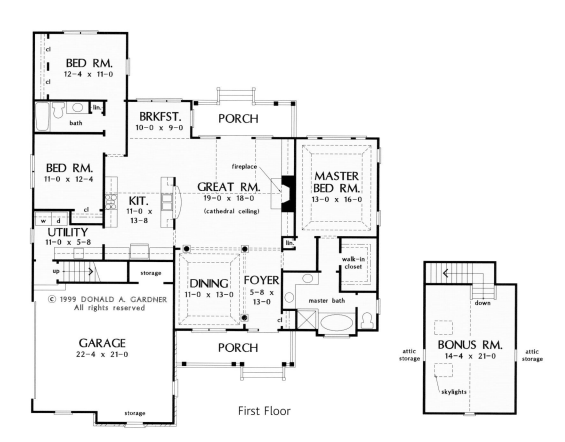

BED RM.
12-4 x 11-0

bath

BED RM.
11-0 x 12-4

KIT.
11-0 x
13-8

BRKFST.
10-0 x 9-0

PORCH

fireplace

GREAT RM.
19-0 x 18-0
(cathedral ceiling)

MASTER
BED RM.
13-0 x 16-0

UTILITY
11-0 x 5-8

w d

storage

up

DINING
11-0 x 13-0

FOYER
5-8 x
13-0

walk-in
closet

master bath

GARAGE
22-4 x 21-0

PORCH

storage

First Floor

down

BONUS RM.
14-4 x 21-0

attic
storage

attic
storage

skylights

Stone, siding, multiple gables and eye-catching windows contribute to the warm Craftsman style. A sophisticated tray ceiling and columns highlight the formal dining room, while the great room and kitchen enjoy a soaring cathedral ceiling. Built-ins border the fireplace in the great room, where a clerestory dormer brings in an abundance of natural light.

Idlewild

Donald A. Gardner Architects, Inc.
CHPDG01-831
1-888-840-6020

Bedrooms: 3
Bath: 2
Width: 55'8"
Depth: 64'10"
1st Floor: 1858 sq ft
Total Living: 1858 sq ft
Bonus Room: 365 sq ft
Foundation: Crawl Space*
Price Code: D

*Other options available. See page 175.

Rear Elevation

www.craftsmandreamhomes.com   35

CHATHAM
cornerstone designs, llc

Embodying the essence of seaboard charm, the *Chatham's* shingle-style gables, gambrels, columns, turrets, balconies and verandas entice visitors to approach.

One is immediately drawn from the traditional foyer into the spectacular grand circular rotunda with its domed stained-glass ceiling and compass rose floor. The two-story great room beyond, with its curved bay window, anchors the expansive family living area.

Formal living and dining rooms provide for grand entertaining, while the intimate library and study allow for quiet activities. Service spaces including a butlery, mud room with elevator, and back stair enhance the home's functionality.

The master suite is a magnificent private retreat, while the children's suites are highlighted by playful and unique spaces. A home theater, game room, laundry and crafts room round out the upper floor.

Above:
The formal dining room's pairs of double French doors, triple-coffered ceiling, painted wainscots, crown moldings and connecting butler's pantry convey a sense of traditional luxury.

Right:
Combining five-star luxury and practical comforts, the master bath's soaking tub, travertine floors and columns, gilded ceiling coffers, spacious double closets and vanities, step-out balcony and stacked washer-dryer has it all.

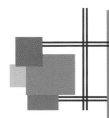

Craftsman's Corner

An overwhelming sense of openness grants a Craftsman feel to this estate home.

Above:
The round bay of the spectacular family room is perfect for a piano, while dark-stained casework provides warmth and intimate scale.

Right:
A gourmet's dream, the grand kitchen features every modern convenience in a spacious layout designed for multiple chefs and culinary entertaining.

Exteriors:
(*Front*) The *Chatham* is a grand expression of traditional east-coast shingle-style design updated for the twenty-first century.
(*Rear*) Distinctive bays, columns, playful porches and elegant expanses of white trim enliven the *Chatham's* expressive rear elevation.

© CornerStone Designs, LLC.

Rear Elevation

CornerStone Designs, LLC

CHPCD01-M7550A4S-0
1-888-840-6020

Bedrooms:	5
Bath:	5-1/2
Width:	95'4"
Depth:	135'0"
1st Floor:	3400 sq ft
2nd Floor:	4500 sq ft
Living Area:	7900 sq ft
Foundation:	Crawl Space
Price Code:	O

Photographed home may have been modified from the original construction documents.

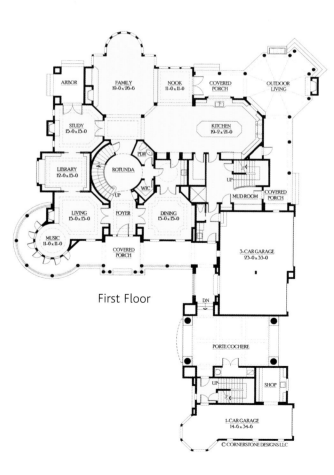

First Floor

Second Floor

© The Sater Design Collection, Inc.

Gables, decorative fretwork, multi-paned windows and a charming front porch invite visitors inside. The foyer opens into the kitchen, great and dining rooms. The cozy great room features a warming fireplace and two French doors to the rear porch. The master suite features a private porch, spacious bath and walk-in closet. Two secondary bedrooms share a bath and one room accesses a sun deck.

Wedgewood
The Sater Design Collection, Inc.
CHPDS01-6841
1-888-840-6020

Bedrooms:	3
Bath:	2
Width:	44'0"
Depth:	40'0"
1st Floor:	1342 sq ft
2nd Floor:	511 sq ft
Lower Level:	33 sq ft
Living Area:	1886 sq ft
Foundation:	Island Basement
Price Code:	E

First Floor

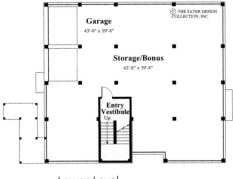

Lower Level

Second Floor

Rear Elevation

Gables accented with cedar shakes join with a shed dormer to create a charming cottage exterior. An angled counter, built-in cabinetry and French doors add a custom-styled touch to the interior. The absence of two walls in the dining room gives the feeling of airiness to the common rooms.

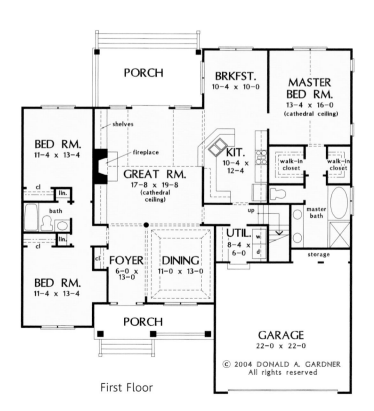

PORCH

BRKFST.
10-4 x 10-0

MASTER BED RM.
13-4 x 16-0
(cathedral ceiling)

BED RM.
11-4 x 13-4

shelves

fireplace

KIT.
10-4 x 12-4

walk-in closet

walk-in closet

cl

lin.

GREAT RM.
17-8 x 19-8
(cathedral ceiling)

up

master bath

bath

lin.

cl

UTIL.
8-4 x 6-0

w

d

FOYER
6-0 x 13-0

DINING
11-0 x 13-0

cl

storage

BED RM.
11-4 x 13-4

PORCH

GARAGE
22-0 x 22-0

First Floor

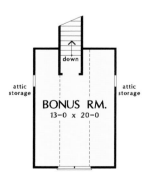

down

attic storage

attic storage

BONUS RM.
13-0 x 20-0

Prairiefield

Donald A. Gardner Architects, Inc.

CHPDG01-1069
1-888-840-6020

Bedrooms:	3
Bath:	2
Width:	54'4"
Depth:	59'0"
1st Floor:	1965 sq ft
Total Living:	1965 sq ft
Bonus Room:	260 sq ft
Foundation:	Crawl Space*
Price Code:	D

*Other options available. See page 175.

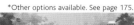

Rear Elevation

SATCHWELL

donald a. gardner architects, inc.

Graceful arches contrast with high gables for a stunning exterior on this Craftsman home. Windows with decorative transoms and several French doors flood the open floor plan with natural light.

Elegant tray ceilings in the dining room and master bedroom, along with cathedral ceilings in the bedroom/study, great room, kitchen and breakfast area, create architectural interest and enhance visual space. While a screened porch allows for comfortable outdoor entertaining and relaxation, a bonus room lies near two additional bedrooms and offers flexibility. Additional space in the garage provides convenient storage.

Above Right:
A two-tiered, stone fireplace and built-in shelves showcase custom details, while French doors and transoms flood the great room with natural light.
Right:
Wainscoting and crown molding adorn the formal dining room, creating an elegant place for meals.
Exteriors:
(Front) Stone and siding provide an eye-catching yet low-maintenance exterior.
(Rear) The screened porch off the breakfast and great room brings the outdoors in, serving as an ideal location for summer meals.

Rear Elevation

Donald A. Gardner
Architects, Inc.
CHPDG01-967
1-888-840-6020

Bedrooms: 4
Bath: 3
Width: 64'10"
Depth: 59'6"
1st Floor: 2097 sq ft
Living Area: 2097 sq ft
Foundation: Crawl Space*
Price Code: E

*Other options available. See page 175

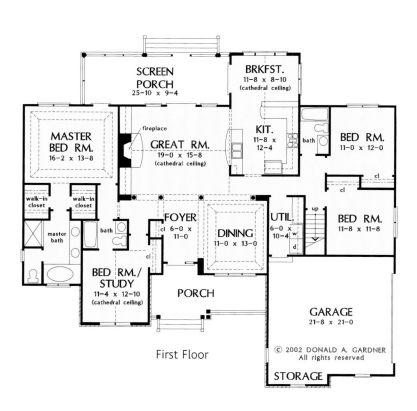

SCREEN PORCH
25-10 x 9-4

BRKFST.
11-8 x 8-10
(cathedral ceiling)

fireplace

GREAT RM.
19-0 x 15-8
(cathedral ceiling)

KIT.
11-8 x 12-4

bath

BED RM.
11-0 x 12-0

MASTER BED RM.
16-2 x 13-8

walk-in closet

walk-in closet

master bath

bath

FOYER
cl 6-0 x 11-0

DINING
11-0 x 13-0

UTIL.
6-0 x 10-4

cl

cl

up

BED RM.
11-8 x 11-8

BED RM./ STUDY
11-4 x 12-10
(cathedral ceiling)

PORCH

GARAGE
21-8 x 21-0

First Floor

STORAGE

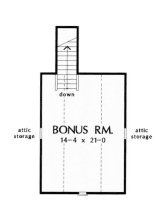

down

attic storage

BONUS RM.
14-4 x 21-0

attic storage

© 2004 Frank Betz Associates, Inc.

Accents like board-and-batten shutters and fieldstone generate a distinctive warmth on the *Berkeley Heights'* façade. Its kitchen, breakfast and family room share a common space for gatherings. Growing families and guests will appreciate the option for an additional level that includes another bedroom, bath and recreational room.

Berkeley Heights

Frank Betz Associates, Inc.

CHPFB01-3890

1-888-840-6020

Bedrooms:	4
Bath:	3-1/2
Width:	60'0"
Depth:	83'4"
1st Floor:	2433 sq ft
Living Area:	2433 sq ft
Opt. 2nd Floor:	632 sq ft
Foundation:	Slab, Crawl Space or Basement
Price Code:	H

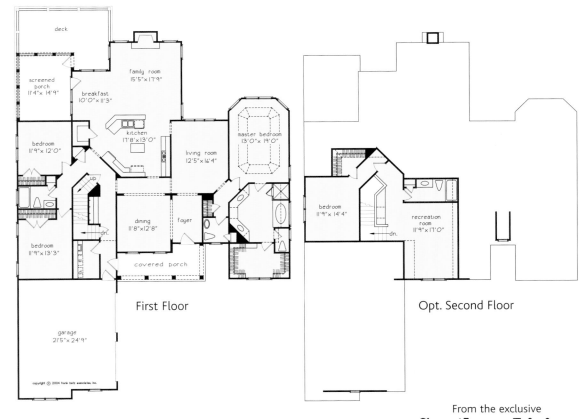

First Floor

Opt. Second Floor

Rear Elevation

From the exclusive

Southern Living

Design Collection

© The Sater Design Collection, Inc.

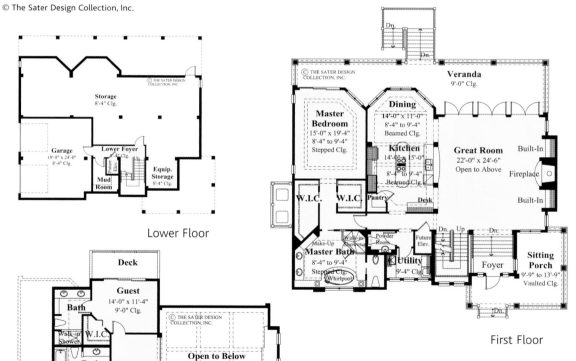

Lower Floor

Storage
8'-4" Clg.

Garage
18'-8" x 24'-0"
8'-4" Clg.

Lower Foyer
Up
Mud
Room

Equip.
Storage
8'-4" Clg.

Second Floor

Deck

Guest
14'-0" x 11'-4"
9'-0" Clg.

Bath

Walk-in
Shower

W.I.C.

Bath

W.I.C

Guest
14'-9" x 11'-10"
Vaults to 9'-0" Clg.

Loft
26'-8" x 12'-9"
9'-0" Clg.

Open to Below
18'-1" to 19'-1"
Stepped Clg.

Open To
Below

Dn.

First Floor

Dn.

Dn.

Veranda
9'-0" Clg.

Master
Bedroom
15'-0" x 19'-4"
8'-4" to 9'-4"
Stepped Clg.

Dining
14'-0" x 11'-0"
8'-4" to 9'-4"
Beamed Clg.

Kitchen
14'-0" x 15'-0"
8'-4" to 9'-4"
Beamed Clg.

Great Room
22'-0" x 24'-6"
Open to Above

Built-In

Fireplace

Built-In

W.I.C.   W.I.C.

Pantry   Desk

Make-Up

Walk-in
Shower

Powder
Room

Master Bath
8'-4" to 9'-4"
Stepped Clg.
Whirlpool

Utility
9'-4" Clg.

Future
Elev.

Dn. Up   Dn.

Foyer

Sitting
Porch
9'-9" to 13'-9"
Vaulted Clg.

Dn.

Gables, decorative shutters and fretwork, Doric columns and a charming front porch enhance the exterior. Steps lead down to the great room, which boasts a two-story ceiling, three sets of French doors and a massive fireplace, flanked by built-in shelves. The gourmet kitchen features a centered cooktop island and walk-in pantry. On the upper level, two bedrooms feature full baths, walk-in closets and access to a sun deck.

Cascade Ridge

The Sater Design Collection, Inc.

CHPDS01-6802
1-888-840-6020

Bedrooms:	3
Bath:	3-1/2
Width:	56'0"
Depth:	54'0"
1st Floor:	2118 sq ft
2nd Floor:	929 sq ft
Living Area:	3328 sq ft
Foundation:	Island Basement
Price Code:	H

Rear Elevation

A unique mixture of stone, siding and windows create character in this Arts and Crafts design. Columns, decorative railing and a metal roof add architectural interest to an intimate porch. An elegant, curved staircase highlights the grand two-story foyer and great room. Light from the clerestory floods both the great room and second-floor loft with light.

Wicklow

Donald A. Gardner Architects, Inc.
CHPDG01-950
1-888-840-6020

Bedrooms:	3
Bath:	2-1/2
Width:	44'4"
Depth:	54'0"
1st Floor:	1542 sq ft
2nd Floor:	752 sq ft
Total Living:	2294 sq ft
Bonus Room:	370 sq ft
Foundation:	Crawl Space*
Price Code:	E

*Other options available. See page 175.

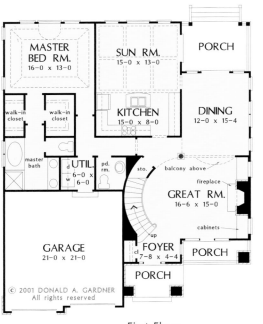

First Floor

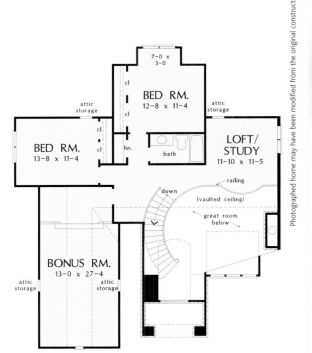

Second Floor

Rear Elevation

© 2004 Donald A. Gardner, Inc.

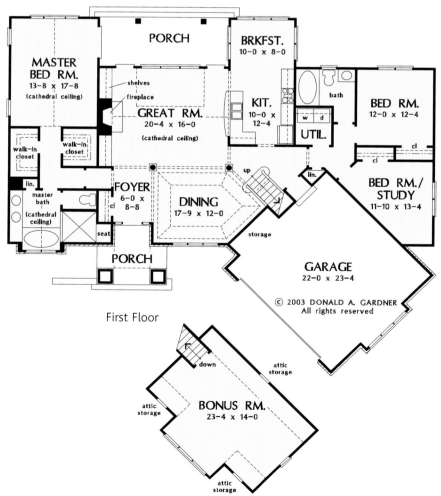

PORCH

MASTER BED RM.
13-8 x 17-8
(cathedral ceiling)

BRKFST.
10-0 x 8-0

shelves
fireplace

KIT.
10-0 x 12-4

bath

w d

UTIL.

BED RM.
12-0 x 12-4

GREAT RM.
20-4 x 16-0
(cathedral ceiling)

walk-in closet

walk-in closet

lin.

master bath
(cathedral ceiling)

seat

cl

FOYER
6-0 x 8-8

cl

DINING
17-9 x 12-0

up

lin.

BED RM./ STUDY
11-10 x 13-4

cl

cl

storage

PORCH

GARAGE
22-0 x 23-4

First Floor

down

attic storage

attic storage

BONUS RM.
23-4 x 14-0

attic storage

Cedar shake and stone add Old-World character to this Craftsman cottage. Remarkably open, the floor plan allows every common room to take advantage of rear views. Columns define the dining room, and the tray ceiling expands it. A cathedral ceiling extends from the fireplace to the serving bar. Other features include built-in cabinetry, a bonus room and French doors.

Gadberry

Donald A. Gardner Architects, Inc.
CHPDG01-1042
1-888-840-6020

Bedrooms:	3
Bath:	2
Width:	67'4"
Depth:	57'8"
1st Floor:	1986 sq ft
Total Living:	1986 sq ft
Bonus Room:	376 sq ft
Foundation:	Crawl Space*
Price Code:	D

*Other options available. See page 175.

Rear Elevation

HARTFORD SPRINGS
frank betz associates, inc.

From the Southern Living® Design Collection—Thoughtful details are what make *Hartford Springs* a unique and well-designed home. Two decks are situated on the back of the home: a handy grilling porch located off the kitchen, as well as a full-sized sunning deck. A crackling fire is the backdrop for family time spent in the vaulted keeping room. The master suite includes a roomy sitting area with access to the deck. His-and-her walk-in closets are carefully placed off the master bath, providing a more peaceful environment in the suite. Additionally, the master bath includes a separate tub and shower as well as dual sinks. Each bedroom upstairs features a walk-in closet and direct access to a bathroom. A spacious teen suite could also make the perfect playroom for little ones.

Above:
The built-in cabinets and dramatic fireplace set the tone for this stunning home.
Right:
Panelled walls mixed with a beamed ceiling show off its special features.

Craftsman's Corner

Decorative brackets, shed dormers and the use of stone comprise this Craftsman home's exterior.

Above Left and Right:
Simply amazing is the only way to describe the master suite and sitting room.

Right:
The coffered ceilings, hardwood floors and use of color make this dining room warm and inviting.

Exterior:
(Front) With a stunning center gable this striking exterior also features box-bay windows and metal roofing to grant extra allure.

© 2003 Frank Betz Associates, Inc.

Rear Elevation

Frank Betz Associates, Inc.

CHPFB01-3824
1-888-840-6020

Bedrooms:	4
Bath:	3-1/2
Width:	73'0"
Depth:	66'10"
1st Floor:	2504 sq ft
2nd Floor:	1467 sq ft
Living Area:	3971 sq ft
Foundation:	Crawl Space or Basement
Price Code:	I

Photographed home may have been modified from the original construction documents.

First Floor

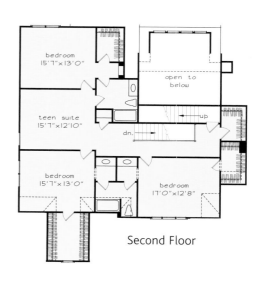

Second Floor

From the exclusive

Southern Living
Design Collection

© 2003 Frank Betz Associates, Inc.

Unique details are what distinguish this home from its other two-story counterparts. A barrel-vaulted ceiling canopies the hallway leading from the foyer to the family room. A separate entrance located on the side of the Ventura, enters through the laundry room—perfect for the daily comings and goings of family members.

Ventura

Frank Betz Associates, Inc.

CHPFB01-3799
1-888-840-6020

Bedrooms:	4
Bath:	3-1/2
Width:	46'4"
Depth:	66'0"
1st Floor:	1243 sq ft
2nd Floor:	1474 sq ft
Living Area:	2717 sq ft
Foundation:	Crawl Space or Basement
Price Code:	H

Rear Elevation

copyright © 2003 frank betz associates, inc.

Garage 20⁹ x 21⁹

First Floor

Second Floor

© CornerStone Designs, LLC.

This charming Craftsman packs a lot of punch into a compact footprint. Bays, brackets and board & batten siding enliven the façade. High windows fill the foyer with light. The open floor plan connects the great room, dining room and island kitchen with cased openings and pass-throughs. The upstairs features walk-in closets in all bedrooms and a large bonus room.

Brandon
CornerStone Designs
CHPCD01-M2127A2S-0
1-888-840-6020

Bedrooms: 3
Bath: 2-1/2
Width: 32'0"
Depth: 56'0"
1st Floor: 965 sq ft
2nd Floor: 1162 sq ft
Living Area: 2127 sq ft
Foundation: Crawl Space
Price Code: E

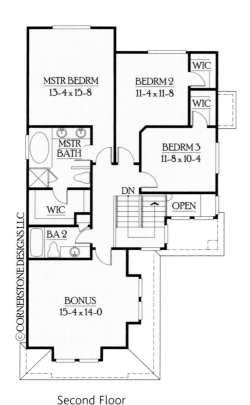

Second Floor

MSTR BEDRM 13-4 x 15-8
BEDRM 2 11-4 x 11-8
WIC
WIC
MSTR BATH
BEDRM 3 11-8 x 10-4
DN
WIC
OPEN
BA 2
BONUS 15-4 x 14-0

© CORNERSTONE DESIGNS LLC

First Floor

DINING 13-4 x 12-8
GREAT ROOM 15-8 x 18-4
KITCHEN 13-4 x 15-8
UP
FOYER
UTILITY
PDR
COV'D PORCH
2-CAR GARAGE 19-4 x 19-8

© CORNERSTONE DESIGNS LLC

Rear Elevation

WESTHAMPTON

frank betz associates, inc.

The distinctive exterior of The *Westhampton* sets the stage for a unique layout. The third garage bay is the perfect spot for a boat or utility storage.

Flanked by decorative columns, the two-story foyer leads to the vaulted family room. The keeping room is directly off the kitchen and breakfast room, offering a fireplace that creates a warm and cozy place to entertain. The master suite, with plenty of wall space and a sitting area, is found on the main level. The master bath has an oversized walk-in closet with built-in storage for linens. Three additional bedrooms have access to multiple bathing areas and walk-in closets. Upstairs a built-in desk gives children a perfect place to do homework.

Above Right:
A vaulted keeping room in close contact with the kitchen lets everyone in on the conversation.
Right:
The foyer and family room are two stories tall, and are highlighted by a coffered ceiling and chandeliers.
Exterior:
(Front) Various roof lines and exterior materials exude a welcoming feeling from the curb.

Rear Elevation

Frank Betz Associates, Inc.

CHPFB01-3767
1-888-840-6020

Bedrooms:	4
Bath:	3-1/2
Width:	72'0"
Depth:	57'0"
1st Floor:	1974 sq ft
2nd Floor:	1038 sq ft
Living Area:	3012 sq ft
Foundation:	Crawl Space or Basement
Price Code:	I

First Floor

Second Floor

© 2002 Donald A. Gardner, Inc.

Blending stone with siding, this cottage has wonderful architectural features: an arch and column porch, metal roof on a box-bay window, decorative vents and striking shed dormer. Built-ins in the great room, tray ceilings in the dining room and master bedroom, and a cooktop island are just a few of the amenities. A study/bedroom and bonus room provide versatility.

Wilshire

Donald A. Gardner Architects, Inc.

CHPDG01-976
1-888-840-6020

Bedrooms:	3
Bath:	2
Width:	53'10"
Depth:	57'8"
1st Floor:	1904 sq ft
Total Living:	1904 sq ft
Bonus Room:	366 sq ft
Foundation:	Crawl Space*
Price Code:	D

*Other options available. See page 175.

Rear Elevation

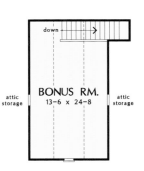

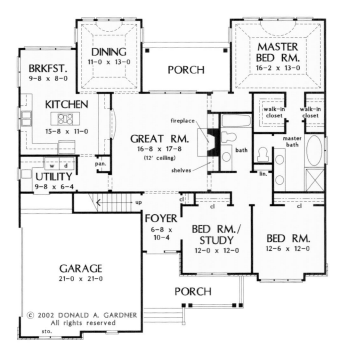

First Floor

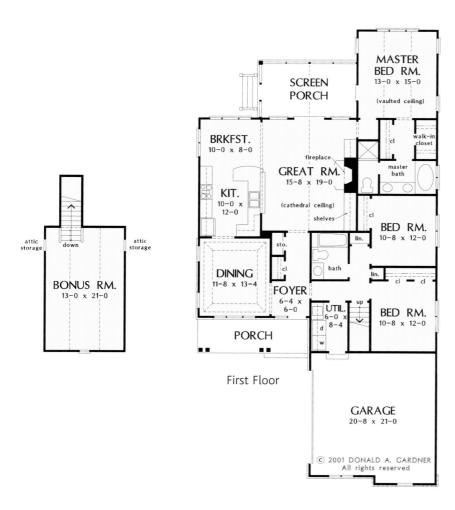

This Arts and Crafts cottage combines stone and stucco to create an Old-World feel. From decorative wood brackets and columns to arched windows and shutters, the details produce architectural interest and absolute charm. Topping the great room is a cathedral ceiling, and a tray ceiling completes the dining room.

Heathrow

Donald A. Gardner Architects, Inc.

CHPDG01-961
1-888-840-6020

Bedrooms:	3
Bath:	2
Width:	40'0"
Depth:	78'4"
1st Floor:	1682 sq ft
Total Living:	1682 sq ft
Bonus Room:	320 sq ft
Foundation:	Crawl Space*
Price Code:	D

*Other options available. See page 175.

Rear Elevation

First Floor plan labels

SCREEN PORCH

MASTER BED RM.
13-0 x 15-0
(vaulted ceiling)

BRKFST.
10-0 x 8-0

walk-in closet

cl

fireplace

GREAT RM.
15-8 x 19-0

master bath

KIT.
10-0 x 12-0

(cathedral ceiling)

shelves

cl

BED RM.
10-8 x 12-0

lin.

sto.

DINING
11-8 x 13-4

cl

bath

lin.

cl   cl

FOYER
6-4 x 6-0

UTIL.
6-0 x 8-4

up

d w

BED RM.
10-8 x 12-0

PORCH

First Floor

GARAGE
20-8 x 21-0

BONUS RM.
13-0 x 21-0

attic storage   attic storage

down

© 2005 Frank Betz Associates, Inc.

The *Stoneleigh Cottage's* open floor plan allows for easy flow between rooms. Upstairs, there are two additional bedrooms, both with walk-in closets and an optional bonus room. The master suite, with its back wall of windows, encompasses one wing of the home.

Stoneleigh Cottage
Frank Betz Associates, Inc.
CHPFB01-3919
1-888-840-6020

Bedrooms:	3
Bath:	2-1/2
Width:	46'0"
Depth:	62'4"
1st Floor:	1448 sq ft
2nd Floor:	527 sq ft
Living Area:	1975 sq ft
Bonus Room:	368 sq ft
Foundation:	Slab, Crawl Space or Basement
Price Code:	G

Rear Elevation

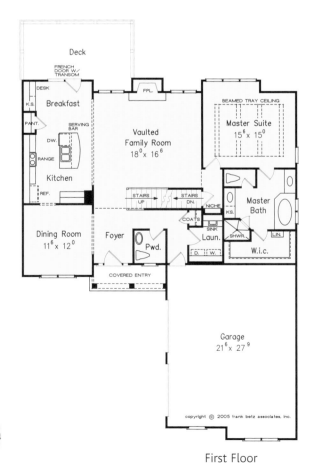

First Floor

Second Floor

This cottage combines stone, siding and cedar shake to create striking curb appeal. The interior features an open floor plan with high ceilings, columns and bay windows. The master suite features a tray ceiling in the bedroom, and on the opposite side of the home, an additional bedroom could be a second master suite. The flexible bonus room awaits expansion.

Longleaf

Donald A. Gardner Architects, Inc.

CHPDG01-802
1-888-840-6020

Bedrooms:	3
Bath:	3
Width:	62'6"
Depth:	57'2"
1st Floor:	1971 sq ft
Total Living:	1971 sq ft
Bonus Room:	358 sq ft
Foundation:	Crawl Space*
Price Code:	D

*Other options available. See page 175.

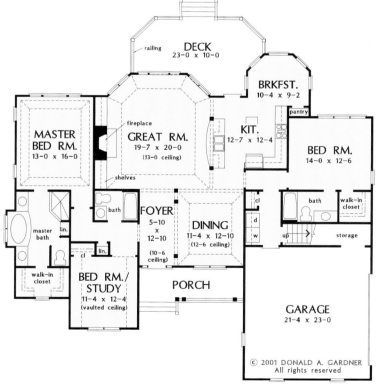

DECK
23-0 x 10-0

railing

BRKFST.
10-4 x 9-2

pantry

fireplace

GREAT RM.
19-7 x 20-0
(13-0 ceiling)

KIT.
12-7 x 12-4

MASTER BED RM.
13-0 x 16-0

shelves

BED RM.
14-0 x 12-6

cl

bath

walk-in closet

master bath

lin.

bath

FOYER
5-10 x 12-10
(10-6 ceiling)

DINING
11-4 x 12-10
(12-6 ceiling)

d

w

up

storage

walk-in closet

cl

lin.

BED RM./ STUDY
11-4 x 12-4
(vaulted ceiling)

PORCH

GARAGE
21-4 x 23-0

First Floor

7-10 x 4-2

down

attic storage

attic storage

BONUS RM.
13-4 x 18-10

Rear Elevation

RUSTIC CRAFTSMAN

The Dogwood Ridge; See page 104

Calling upon nature for their exterior materials, these RUSTIC CRAFTSMAN homes elegantly combine natural materials with fine Craftsman details. Rugged and attractive, these plans are ideal for mountain settings or those not seeking the close confines of city life. Featuring porches, stone and timber details, low rooflines and open layouts, this section brings the Craftsman look to life.

© CornerStone Designs, LLC.

First Floor

Second Floor

Third Floor

A magnificent mansion, this grand lodge-style estate conveys the majesty of its namesake. A powerful stone base sets the stage for its strong shingled forms. Broad wraparound porches command views of nature, while bold columns, bays, brackets and trim create a timeless image. The open floor plan centers on the great room hearth. The third-floor office is a flexible getaway.

Yellowstone
CornerStone Designs
CHPCD01-M6575A4S-0
1-888-840-6020

Bedrooms:	4
Bath:	4 Full, 2 Half
Width:	118'0"
Depth:	61'6"
1st Floor:	3413 sq ft
2nd Floor:	3038 sq ft
3rd Floor:	974 sq ft
Living Area:	7425 sq ft
Foundation:	Crawl Space
Price Code:	O

Rear Elevation

© 2005 Frank Betz Associates, Inc.

The spaciousness of the *Summerlake* offers many amenities usually reserved for much larger homes. The luxurious main-level master suite offers a built-in niche, drying area and connecting his-and-her closets with a dressing mirror. An additional bedroom on the main level can be used as such or converted to a study.

Summerlake

Frank Betz Associates, Inc.

CHPFB04-3952
1-888-840-6020

Bedrooms: 4
Bath: 3
Width: 62'4"
Depth: 64'0"
1st Floor: 2145 sq ft
2nd Floor: 754 sq ft
Living Area: 2899 sq ft
Bonus Room: 385 sq ft
Foundation: Slab, Crawl Space or Basement
Price Code: I

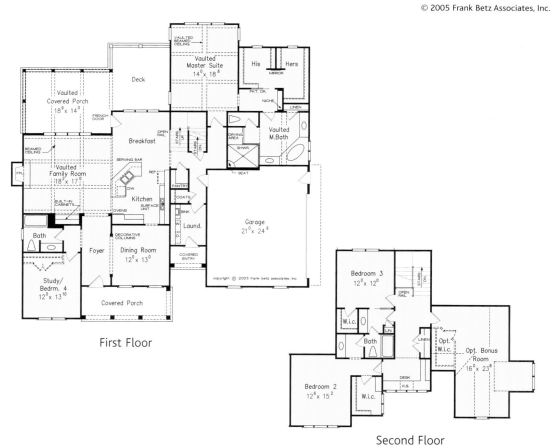

First Floor

Second Floor

Rear Elevation

© CornerStone Designs, LLC.

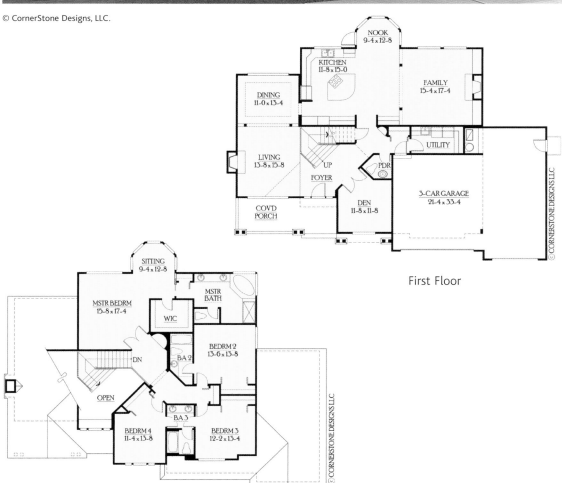

First Floor

Second Floor

E legant gabled arches highlight the façade of this graceful Craftsman-style home. The vaulted front porch invites you into the two-story foyer with its dramatic angled staircase. Cased openings, half walls and columns define spaces and add detail. The generous master suite plus three secondary bedrooms and work-at-home den offer plenty of room for large families.

Trillium Lane
CornerStone Designs
CHPCD01-M3215A3F-0
1-888-840-6020

Bedrooms:	4
Bath:	3-1/2
Width:	70'0"
Depth:	55'0"
1st Floor:	1686 sq ft
2nd Floor:	1529 sq ft
Living Area:	3215 sq ft
Foundation:	Crawl Space
Price Code:	F

Rear Elevation

CROWNE CANYON

donald a. gardner architects, inc.

A stunning center dormer with arched window and decorative wood brackets cap the entry to this extraordinary hillside estate.

Exposed wood beams enhance the magnificent cathedral ceilings of the foyer, great room, dining room, master bedroom and screened porch, while ten-foot ceilings top the remainder of the first floor. The great room takes in scenic rear views through a wall of windows shared by the media/rec room. Fireplaces add warmth and ambience to the great room, media/rec room, screened porch and the master suite.

The kitchen is complete with its center island cook-top, pantry and ample room for two or more cooks.

Above Right:
Exposed wooden beams frame the great room's entryway, while a stone fireplace becomes a striking focal point.
Right:
The sitting area just off the master bedroom features a fireplace and the convenience of an additional relaxing space.
Exteriors:
(Front) The motorcourt introduces this high-style yet low-maintenance hillside home.
(Rear) With a rear wall of windows and porches, this home really captures the views.

Rear Elevation

DONALD A. GARDNER ARCHITECTS, INC.
CHPDG01-732-D
1-888-840-6020

Bedrooms:	5
Bath:	4-1/2
Width:	106'5"
Depth:	104'2"
1st Floor:	3040 sq ft
Basement:	1736 sq ft
Living Area:	4776 sq ft
Foundation:	Hillside Walkout
Price Code:	J

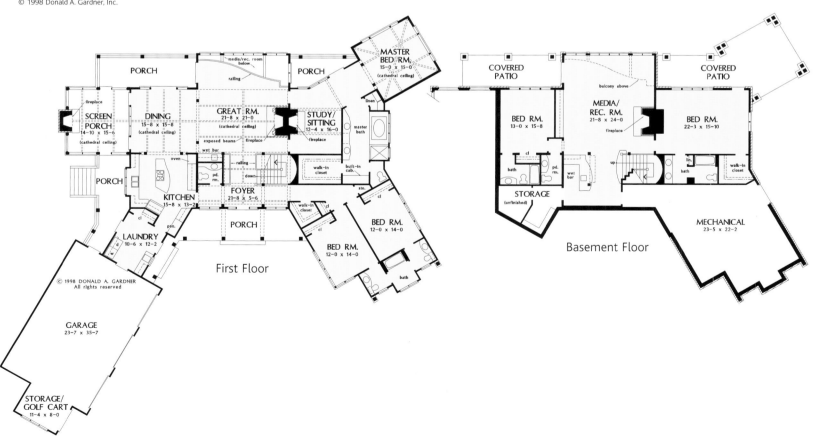

First Floor

Basement Floor

© 2005 Donald A. Gardner, Inc.

olumns accent the welcoming front porch, while the side-entry garage naturally blends into the home's impressive façade. Perfect for overnight guests, the bedroom/study is complete with a walk-in closet and full bath. Open to the kitchen and accessing a rear porch, the great room naturally flows from one space to another.

Bailey

Donald A. Gardner Architects, Inc.

CHPDG01-1115
1-888-840-6020

Bedrooms:	4
Bath:	3
Width:	56'8"
Depth:	69'8"
1st Floor:	2051 sq ft
Total Living:	2051 sq ft
Bonus Room:	420 sq ft
Foundation:	Crawl Space*
Price Code:	E

*Other options available. See page 175.

Rear Elevation

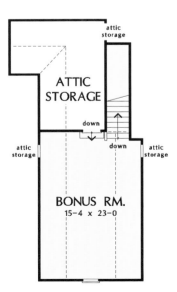

ATTIC STORAGE

attic storage

down   down

attic storage   attic storage

BONUS RM.
15-4 x 23-0

First Floor

Second Floor

- Porch
  13'-6" x 4'-10"
- Master Suite
  12'-8" x 17'-8"
  10'-0" Tray Clg.
- Open to Below
  18'-0" Vaulted Clg.
- W.I.C.
- Overlook
- Linen
- Master Bath
  8'-0" Clg.
- Whirlpool
- Dn.
- Porch

© THE SATER DESIGN COLLECTION, INC.

Lower Level

- Covered Porch
  13'-0" X 9'-4"
- Covered Porch
  26'-0" X 5'-10"
- Firewood Storage
- 2 Car Garage
  8'-4" Clg.
- Bonus/ Storage
- Ski/Equip. Storage
- Mud Area

© THE SATER DESIGN COLLECTION, INC.

First Floor

- Deck
  13'-6" x 4'-6"
- Porch
  13'-0" x 4'-4"
- Covered Porch
  26'-0" x 6'-0"
- Dining
  11'-0" x 12'-8"
  11'-0" Tray Clg.
- Fireplace
- Bedroom 3
  11'-6" x 12'-0"
  10'-0" Clg.
- Great Room
  15'-0" x 19'-6"
  Vaulted Clg.
- Porch
  5'-0" x 13'-6"
- Built-ins
- Kitchen
  11'-0" x 12'-0"
  10'-0" Clg.
- Bedroom 2
  12'-10" x 12'-0"
  10'-0" Clg.
- Closet
- Tub
- Up.
- Util.
- Closet
- Dn.
- Foyer
- Up.
- Entry

© THE SATER DESIGN COLLECTION, INC.

Decorative shutters, multiple decks and covered porches combine with a bold mix of textures to create a refined, rustic feel. Built-ins, a fireplace and extensive views through a wall of windows add to the appeal of the great room. Wrapping counters, an angled double sink and ample storage enhance the kitchen. The master suite enjoys privacy, a spacious bath, walk-in closet and access to a private-covered porch.

Buckhurst Lodge
The Sater Design Collection, Inc.
CHPDS01-6807
1-888-840-6020

Bedrooms:	3
Bath:	2
Width:	48'0"
Depth:	42'0"
1st Floor:	1383 sq ft
2nd Floor:	595 sq ft
Living Area:	1978 sq ft
Foundation:	Island Basement
Price Code:	E

Rear Elevation

© The Sater Design Collection, Inc.

This home features a charming front porch, which supports a distinctive front gable. The great room boasts built-in cabinetry, a cozy fireplace and French doors to the rear porch. The kitchen offers a center work island with prep sink, built-in work desk and easy access to the dining and great rooms. The master retreat has two walk-in closets, a luxe bath and access to the rear porch.

Lunden Valley

The Sater Design Collection, Inc.
CHPDS01-7050
1-888-840-6020

Bedrooms:	3
Bath:	2-1/2
Width:	70'6"
Depth:	76'6"
1st Floor:	2555 sq ft
Living Area:	2555 sq ft
Foundation:	Crawl Space
Price Code:	G

First Floor

Rear Elevation

© 2004 Frank Betz Associates, Inc.

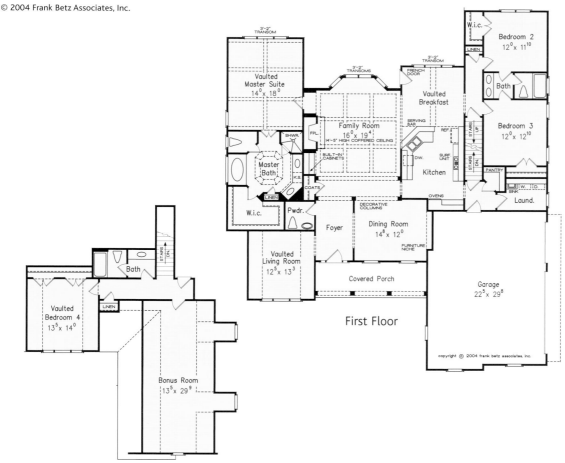

First Floor

Opt. Second Floor

The *Maplewood's* inviting exterior is just a taste of what's waiting inside. Transom windows along the back of the home welcome in plenty of sunshine, brightening each room. A coffered ceiling, fireplace and built-in cabinetry in the family room make for an attractive center point of the home.

Maplewood

Frank Betz Associates, Inc.

CHPFB01-3878

1-888-840-6020

Bedrooms: 4
Bath: 3-1/2
Width: 61'0"
Depth: 70'6"
1st Floor: 2400 sq ft
Living Area: 2400 sq ft
Opt. 2nd Floor: 845 sq ft
Foundation: Slab, Crawl Space or Basement
Price Code: G

Rear Elevation

RIVA RIDGE

donald a. gardner architects, inc.

A stylish blend of cottage living and lavish architectural detail, the *Riva Ridge* embraces the outdoors in a comfortable and practical floor plan. An exciting ensemble of siding and stone, copper roofing and a detached garage gives this Craftsman home irresistible curb appeal.

The interior is immediately welcoming with a large, open foyer that gracefully flows into the great room. Featuring a fireplace and built-in shelves on one side, the great room possesses striking architectural detail. With a rear wall of windows, the room is bathed in sunlight.

The basement level features two bedrooms with full baths, large rec room and outdoor covered patio.

Above:
A vaulted ceiling, rear wall of windows and stone fireplace add exciting architectural detail to the great room.
Right:
Stainless-steel appliances and black countertops complement the rustic-looking cabinetry in the kitchen.

Craftsman's Corner

The sloping foundation of this mountain home showcases a Craftsman trait of yesterday.

Above:
The dining room overlooks the screen porch and rear deck so views are long and scenic.

Right:
Enjoying alfresco meals or watching sunsets is a breeze on the side porch.

Exteriors:
(Front) A natural blend of stone and siding combines with a copper roof and attractive garage doors for an exciting façade.

(Rear) The expansive lower level walks out onto a covered patio for an additional entertaining space.

Rear Elevation

Donald A. Gardner
Architects, Inc.
CHPAL01-5013
1-888-840-6020

Bedrooms:	4
Bath:	4
Width:	60'6"
Depth:	41'7"
1st Floor:	1428 sq ft
Basement Floor:	835 sq ft
Living Area:	2263 sq ft
Foundation:	Hillside Walkout
Price Code:	O

First Floor

Basement Floor

© 2002 Donald A. Gardner, Inc.

This home combines stone, cedar shake and siding for an outstanding exterior. Ushering light into an upstairs bedroom and the two-story foyer, triple dormers lie above a cozy front porch. Columns in the dining room and a tray ceiling in the master suite add architectural interest, while a kitchen island and butler's pantry add convenience.

Coltraine

Donald A. Gardner Architects, Inc.
CHPDG01-966
1-888-840-6020

Bedrooms:	3
Bath:	2-1/2
Width:	59'0"
Depth:	47'8"
1st Floor:	1856 sq ft
2nd Floor:	610 sq ft
Total Living:	2466 sq ft
Bonus Room:	322 sq ft
Foundation:	Crawl Space*
Price Code:	E

*Other options available. See page 175.

First Floor

Second Floor

Rear Elevation

© 2003 Frank Betz Associates, Inc.

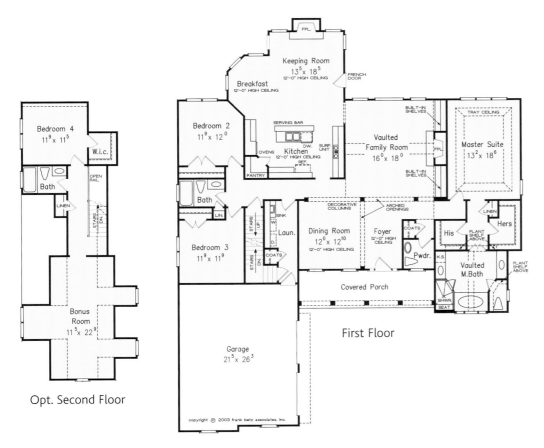

Opt. Second Floor

First Floor

Bedroom 4 11⁹ x 11⁵

Bath

Bonus Room 11⁵ x 22⁹

Keeping Room 13⁵ x 18⁵ 12'-0" HIGH CEILING

Breakfast 12'-0" HIGH CEILING

Bedroom 2 11⁹ x 12⁰

SERVING BAR

Kitchen 12'-0" HIGH CEILING

OVENS

PANTRY

Bath

Bedroom 3 11⁹ x 11⁹

Laun.

Dining Room 12⁰ x 12¹⁰ 12'-0" HIGH CEILING

Foyer 12'-0" HIGH CEILING

Vaulted Family Room 16⁰ x 18⁰

Master Suite 13² x 18⁶

TRAY CEILING

His

Hers

Pwdr.

Vaulted M.Bath

Covered Porch

Garage 21⁵ x 26³

copyright © 2003 frank betz associates, inc.

Beamed gables and cedar shake create an appealing Craftsman-style elevation on the *Camden Lake*. Double ovens, a serving bar and a liberally sized pantry make the kitchen a user-friendly room. Its view to the cozy keeping area warms the entire space, creating an inviting environment.

Camden Lake
Frank Betz Associates, Inc.
CHPFB01-3828
1-888-840-6020

Bedrooms:	4
Bath:	3-1/2
Width:	62'6"
Depth:	77'4"
1st Floor:	2395 sq ft
Living Area:	2395 sq ft
Opt. 2nd Floor:	660 sq ft
Foundation:	Crawl Space or Basement
Price Code:	H

Rear Elevation

© 2000 Donald A. Gardner, Inc.

A number of prominent gables, a mixture of straight and arched windows and a combination of stone, siding and cedar shake shingles adorn this charming four-bedroom home. An exciting cathedral ceiling unifies the open great room and kitchen, while a tray ceiling and columns define the dining room.

Nottingham

Donald A. Gardner Architects, Inc.
CHPDG01-854
1-888-840-6020

Bedrooms:	4
Bath:	2
Width:	65'8"
Depth:	67'10"
1st Floor:	2353 sq ft
Total Living:	2353 sq ft
Bonus Room:	353 sq ft
Foundation:	Crawl Space*
Price Code:	E

*Other options available. See page 175.

Rear Elevation

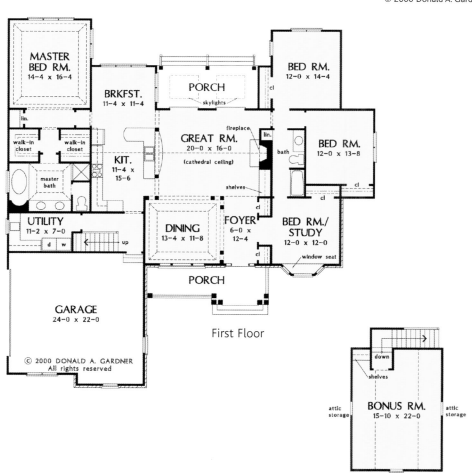

First Floor

BONUS RM.
15-10 x 22-0

© CornerStone Designs, LLC.

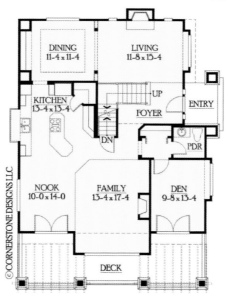

First Floor

DINING
11-4 x 11-4

LIVING
11-8 x 15-4

KITCHEN
13-4 x 13-4

UP

ENTRY

FOYER

DN

PDR

NOOK
10-0 x 14-0

FAMILY
13-4 x 17-4

DEN
9-8 x 13-4

DECK

Second Floor

BEDRM 3
9-8 x 11-4

UTILITY

BONUS
11-4 x 15-4

OPEN

BEDRM 2
9-8 x 11-4

DN

BA 2

WIC

MSTR BATH

MSTR BEDRM
11-4 x 15-4

Lower Level

CRAWL SPACE

UP

3-CAR GARAGE
22-6 x 32-8

The *Touchstone* is a perfect house for a narrow, uphill lot. An efficient garage-under plan with expressive Craftsman detailing, its solid stone base and trellis-topped columns create stunning visual drama. The spacious deck, grand island kitchen, nook, family room, den and large private master suite are all oriented towards the view.

Touchstone
CornerStone Designs
CHPCD01-M2675A3SU-0
1-888-840-6020

Bedrooms:	3
Bath:	2-1/2
Width:	50'0"
Depth:	36'0"
1st Floor:	1334 sq ft
2nd Floor:	1216 sq ft
Lower Level:	125 sq ft
Living Area:	2675 sq ft
Foundation:	Crawl Space
Price Code:	F

Rear Elevation

HENNEFIELD

frank betz associates, inc.

With its board and batten siding, cedar shakes, and cottage stone accents, *Hennefield* makes you feel good every time you see it. The spacious, open interior welcomes you with high ceilings and columns in the foyer and dining room. Built-in cabinets flank the family room fireplace. The kitchen is open to a generous breakfast area and adjoining vaulted keeping room, and features an angled serving bar, large pantry and center island. The master suite provides a soothing sanctuary away from everyday life, where French doors lead to a pampering spa-styled bath. The secondary bedrooms share a bath and are tucked away in their own corner of the home to enhance privacy.

Above:
The vaulted ceiling, built-in bookshelves and a wall of windows make this room open and comfortable.
Right:
Rich cabinetry, marble countertops and hardwood floors are the perfect combination for this state of the art kitchen.

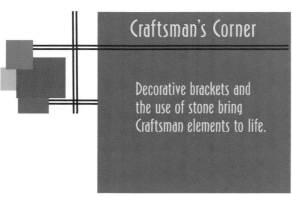

Craftsman's Corner

Decorative brackets and the use of stone bring Craftsman elements to life.

Above:
The open floor plan allows easy interaction between the kitchen, keeping room and family room.

Right:
Decorative columns and arches help frame the dining room.

Exterior:
(Front) Stone and siding coupled with multiple gables give this Craftsman home irresistible curb appeal.

Rear Elevation

Frank Betz Associates, Inc.

CHPFB01-3835
1-888-840-6020

Bedrooms:	4
Bath:	3-1/2
Width:	63'0"
Depth:	67'6"
1st Floor:	2548 sq ft
Living Area:	2548 sq ft
Opt. 2nd Floor:	490 sq ft
Foundation:	Crawl Space or Basement
Price Code:	H

© 2003 Frank Betz Associates, Inc.

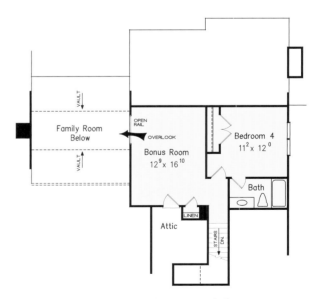

Master Suite 14² x 19⁸

Vaulted Family Room 16⁵ x 18⁰

Breakfast

Vaulted Keeping Room 13⁵ x 14⁹

Kitchen

W.i.c.

Bedroom 2 12⁰ x 11⁰

Bath

Vaulted M.Bath

Foyer 12'-0" HIGH CEILING

Dining Room 12⁰ x 13³ 12'-0" HIGH CEILING

Pwdr.

His   Hers

Laun.

Bedroom 3 12⁸ x 11³

Covered Porch

Garage 22⁷ x 20⁴

First Floor

Family Room Below

Bonus Room 12⁹ x 16¹⁰

Bedroom 4 11² x 12⁰

Attic

Bath

Opt. Second Floor

copyright © 2003 frank betz associates, inc.

The *Hedgerow* offers many luxuries that much larger homes provide. The laundry room offers a side entrance with a built-in bench and hooks, providing the ideal place for shoes, coats and book bags. This main-level master floor plan offers a sitting room with built-in book shelves.

Hedgerow

Frank Betz Associates, Inc.

CHPFB01-3945
1-888-840-6020

Bedrooms:	3
Bath:	2-1/2
Width:	59'0"
Depth:	52'0"
1st Floor:	1769 sq ft
2nd Floor:	555 sq ft
Living Area:	2324 sq ft
Bonus Room:	287 sq ft
Foundation:	Slab, Crawl Space or Basement
Price Code:	H

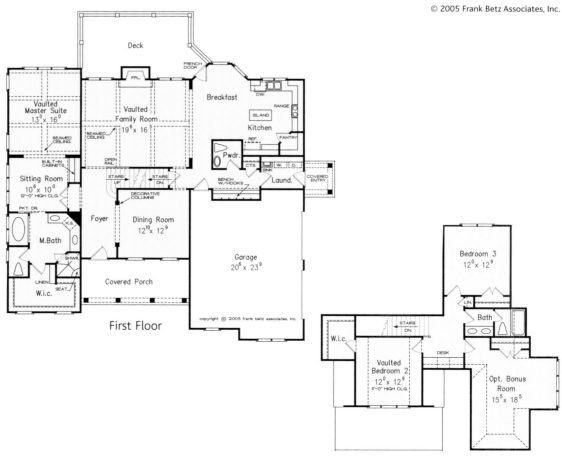

First Floor

Opt. Second Floor

Rear Elevation

© 2001 Donald A. Gardner, Inc.

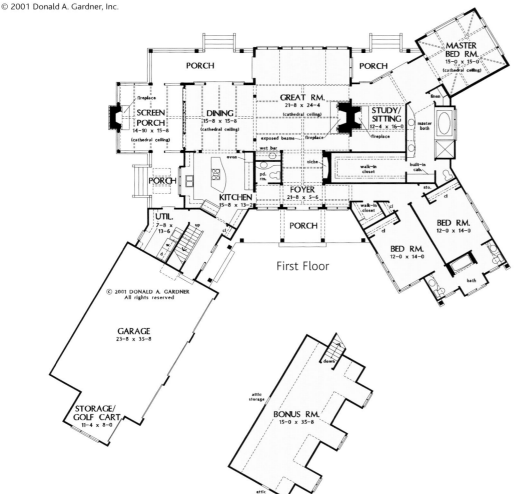

First Floor

An arched entryway mimics the large clerestory above it, while a trio of dormers and multiple gables add architectural interest. Equally impressive, the interior boasts three fireplaces — one within a scenic screened porch. A cathedral ceiling extends from the great room to the screened porch, highlighted by exposed beams. An art niche complements the foyer. Note the wet bar.

Cedar Creek

Donald A. Gardner Architects, Inc.

CHPDG01-959
1-888-840-6020

Bedrooms:	3
Bath:	2-1/2
Width:	106'4"
Depth:	104'1"
1st Floor:	3188 sq ft
Total Living:	3188 sq ft
Bonus Room:	615 sq ft
Foundation:	Crawl Space*
Price Code:	G

*Other options available. See page 175.

Rear Elevation

Tapered architectural columns and unique, mission style windows give this home an original look. A vaulted keeping room is arranged just off the kitchen and breakfast areas of the home with a cozy fireplace and serene backyard views. An optional second floor gives the possibility for an additional bedroom and children's retreat.

Braxton's Creek

Frank Betz Associates, Inc.
CHPFB01-3851
1-888-840-6020

Bedrooms:	4
Bath:	3-1/2
Width:	66'4"
Depth:	83'0"
1st Floor:	2660 sq ft
Living Area:	2660 sq ft
Opt. 2nd Floor:	610 sq ft
Foundation:	Crawl Space or Basement
Price Code:	H

First Floor

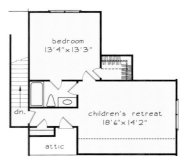

Opt. Second Floor

Rear Elevation

From the exclusive

Southern Living
Design Collection

© CornerStone Designs, LLC.

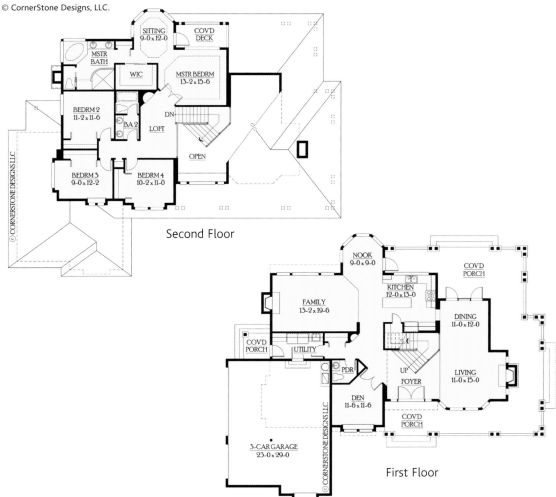

Second Floor

SITTING
9-0 x 12-0

COVD DECK

MSTR BATH

WIC

MSTR BEDRM
13-2 x 15-6

BEDRM 2
11-2 x 11-6

BA 2

LOFT

DN

OPEN

BEDRM 3
9-0 x 12-2

BEDRM 4
10-2 x 11-0

First Floor

NOOK
9-0 x 9-0

KITCHEN
12-0 x 13-0

COVD PORCH

FAMILY
13-2 x 19-6

DINING
11-0 x 12-0

COVD PORCH

UTILITY

PDR

UP

FOYER

LIVING
11-0 x 15-0

DEN
11-6 x 11-6

COVD PORCH

3-CAR GARAGE
23-0 x 29-0

Sweeping vistas of the great outdoors are captured from the grand wrap around porches of the *Chinook*. Its Lodge-Craftsman styling, set off with stone and shingles, conveys a sense of rustic elegance. The open floor plan flows around the dramatic, angled central stair, with the soaring entry foyer incorporating an overlook study loft. The master suite's sitting room and private balcony create a luxurious refuge.

Chinook
CornerStone Designs
CHPCD01-M2770A3S-0
1-888-840-6020

Bedrooms: 4
Bath: 2-1/2
Width: 72'0"
Depth: 62'0"
1st Floor: 1510 sq ft
2nd Floor: 1260 sq ft
Living Area: 2770 sq ft
Foundation: Crawl Space
Price Code: F

Rear Elevation

CEDAR RIDGE
donald a. gardner architects, inc.

The 2005 *Progressive Farmer* Idea House — Living comfortably has never been easier! This gorgeous Craftsman home exposes rich architectural detail throughout the open floor plan. Perfect for those who enjoy outdoor living, this design features copious areas for taking advantage of Mother Nature. A sunroom, rear deck and screened porch are all on the main level, while the lower level boasts a screened porch with summer kitchen, as well as a second covered porch.

Entertaining spaces continue with the spacious great room/dining room and lower-level entertainment room with a wet bar and outdoor summer kitchen. Multiple mud rooms, a large pantry and utility room provide abundant storage space, while a covered walkway ensures dry trips to and from the three-car garage.

Above:
The great room and kitchen are one giant entertaining space that seamlessly flow into one another and grant and open feel to the first floor.
Right:
With an abundance of counter space and cathedral ceiling, the kitchen is truly spacious, and large enough for two cooks.

Craftsman's Corner

Decorative brackets and shed dormers bring out the Craftsman appeal in this spacious home.

Above:
The spacious utility room provides more than enough space for laundry, crafts and ironing clothes.

Right:
The summer kitchen on the lower-level screen porch is the ideal way to enjoy alfresco meals.

Exteriors:
(Front) The Craftsman exterior gives this farmhouse a modern façade, while carved details over the entryway provide a friendly welcome.

(Rear) Spacious porches highlight the rear exterior, providing ample spaces for family gatherings and enjoying pastoral views.

Rear Elevation

DONALD A. GARDNER ARCHITECTS, INC.
CHPDG01-1125-D
1-888-840-6020

Bedrooms:	3
Bath:	4
Width:	62'10"
Depth:	64'2"
1st Floor:	2405 sq ft
Basement:	1273 sq ft
Living Area:	3678 sq ft
Bonus Room:	679 sq ft
Foundation:	Hillside Walkout
Price Code:	O

First Floor

Basement Floor

The PROGRESSIVE FARMER

A mixture of materials enhances the exterior of this hillside walkout, while a deck, screened porch and patio promote outdoor living. With the rear wall comprised of windows and French doors, both levels receive natural light and views. A cathedral ceiling with exposed beams crowns the kitchen and great room, while a built-in, bedroom/study and office add convenience.

Colridge
Donald A. Gardner Architects, Inc.
CHPDG01-1012-D
1-888-840-6020

Bedrooms:	3
Bath:	3
Width:	70'6"
Depth:	59'6"
1st Floor:	1732 sq ft
Basement Floor:	920 sq ft
Total Living:	2652 sq ft
Foundation:	Hillside Walkout
Price Code:	F

Rear Elevation

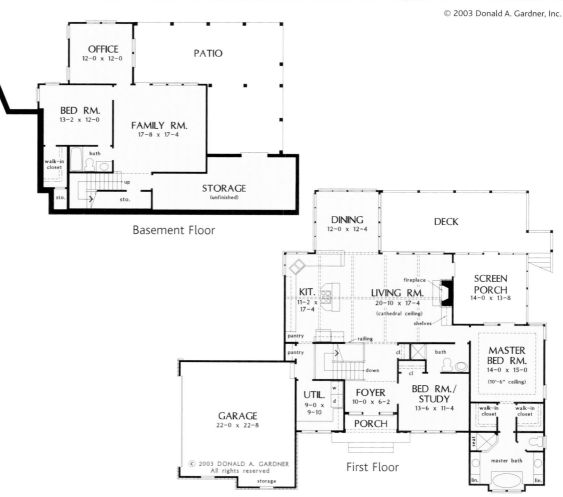

Basement Floor

First Floor

© The Sater Design Collection, Inc.

Porch
30'-6" x 10'-0"

Nook
13'-0" x 9'-4"
10'-0" Flat Clg.

Master Suite
13'-0" x 20'-8"
Tray Ceiling

Bedroom 2
11'-2" x 12'-9"
Tray Ceiling

Kitchen
13'-0" x 12'-0"
Stepped Clg.

Dining Room
12'-8" x 16"-0"
Coffered Clg.

Living Room
17'-8" x 16'-0"
Coffered Clg.

Ent. Center

Bath 2

P.

Art Niche

Art Niche

Fireplace

Art Niche

WIC

WIC

10'-0" Clg.

Foyer
11'-0" Clg. 18'-9" Clg. 11'-0" Clg.

L.

L.

Bedroom 1
16'-6" x 12'-3"
Tray Ceiling

Utility
7'-8' x 12'-0"
10'-0" Clg.

Study/Office
12'-0" x 13'-0"
Stepped Clg.

Book Shelves

Entry
18'-0" x 6'-0"

M. Bath

Walk-in Shower

First Floor

Garage
23'-6" x 23'-0"

©THE SATER DESIGN
COLLECTION, INC.

Art Niche

Dn.

Bedroom 1
13'-2" x 12'-3"
Tray Ceiling

Utility

©THE SATER DESIGN
COLLECTION, INC.

Opt. Basement Stair Location

A clever roofline is punctuated by shutters and a copper-topped office roof. Glass doors expand the dining and living rooms to the rear porch. The large kitchen maintains easy access to the dining room and nook. A study/office has built-in bookshelves and a front yard view. The privacy of the master suite is protected by double entry doors. The master bathroom enjoys double vanities.

Marcella
The Sater Design Collection, Inc.
CHPDS01-7005
1-888-840-6020

Bedrooms: 3
Bath: 2
Width: 70'0"
Depth: 72'0"
1st Floor: 2487 sq ft
Living Area: 2487 sq ft
Foundation: Slab or Basement
Price Code: F

Rear Elevation

Promoting easy living, this home combines Craftsman character with a low maintenance exterior. Art niches, fireplaces and built-in cabinetry add beauty and convenience. The kitchen has a well-located pass-through to the great room, while the master suite features a bay sitting area and custom accents. A spacious deck and porch expand living outdoors.

Edgewater

Donald A. Gardner Architects, Inc.

CHPDG01-1009
1-888-840-6020

Bedrooms:	4
Bath:	3
Width:	70'0"
Depth:	69'10"
1st Floor:	2818 sq ft
Total Living:	2818 sq ft
Foundation:	Crawl Space*
Price Code:	F

*Other options available. See page 175.

Rear Elevation

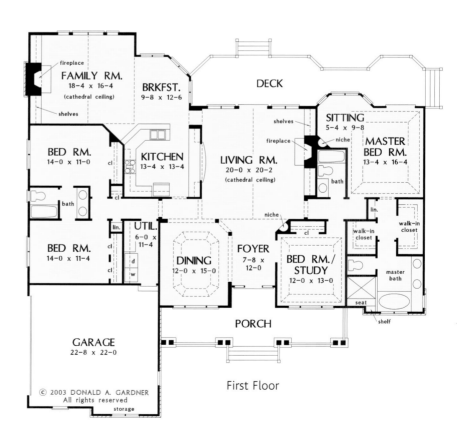

First Floor

© The Sater Design Collection, Inc.

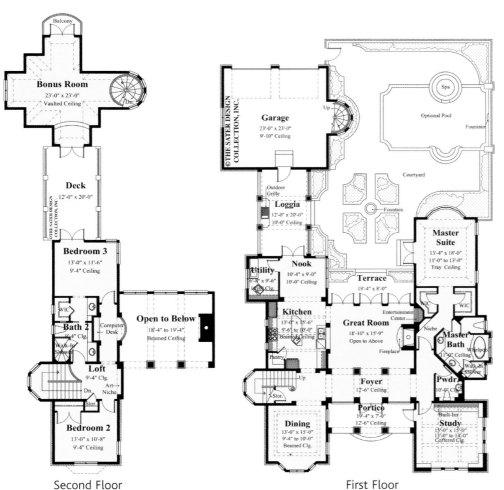

Second Floor

First Floor

Sculpted arcades, terraces and a cupola adorn the exterior. A fireplace anchors the great room, which is extended by the veranda to the outdoors. The gourmet kitchen features a beamed ceiling, walk-in pantry, work island and easy access to the great room. The master suite begins with a sculpted art niche and extends to a private porch.

Edmonton
The Sater Design Collection, Inc.
CHPDS01-8023
1-888-840-6020

Bedrooms:	3
Bath:	2-1/2
Width:	60'6"
Depth:	94'0"
1st Floor:	2117 sq ft
2nd Floor:	652 sq ft
Living Area:	2769 sq ft
Bonus Room:	375 sq ft
Foundation:	Slab or Opt. Basement
Price Code:	G

Rear Elevation

CEDAR CREST
cornerstone designs, llc

The *Cedar Crest's* romantic façade and easy-living floor plan create a dramatic expression of "home".

This Craftsman masterpiece is perfect for a forest or fairway lot. Its wraparound porch adds warmth to the façade and is a great place to watch the world go by. A side-entry garage and decorative shop bay further enhance its curb appeal.

The popular family living layout features vaulted formal living and dining rooms off the volume foyer, complemented by a spacious informal living area with a covered patio that is ideal for outdoor dining.

The angled front stair leads directly to the luxury master suite with its private sitting room and grand bath. A second stair provides quiet access to the children's bedrooms with connecting bath, guest suite with private bath and large vaulted bonus room.

Above:
Dramatic ceiling vaults, wainscots and columns grace the *Cedar Crest's* formal rooms. The built-in hutch is an elegant touch.
Right:
French doors off the foyer open to a productive home office or a quiet refuge for reading and contemplation. Dark-stained crown moldings, wainscots and trim complement the built-in bookshelves and cabinets.

Craftsman's Corner

Low, overhanging eaves and a deep porch showcase true Craftsman traits in this expansive home.

Above:
The generous kitchen and octagonal nook flow together, with dark-stained cabinets and hardwood floors elegantly contrasting with the soft-toned granite countertops and backsplashes with tiled accents.

Right:
The master suite's octagonal sitting room is perfect spot for a luxurious reading nook, or a convenient location for an exercise machine with a great view.

Exteriors:
(Front) The *Cedar Crest's* sweeping roof, broad wrap around porch, powerful columns and bold brackets convey a sense of timeless strength.
(Rear) The covered BBQ patio provides an opportunity for all-season outdoor living.

© CornerStone Designs, LLC.

Rear Elevation

CornerStone Designs

CHPCD01-M4100A3S-0
1-888-840-6020

Bedrooms:	4
Bath:	3-1/2
Width:	90'0"
Depth:	66'6"
1st Floor:	2010 sq ft
2nd Floor:	2090 sq ft
Living Area:	4100 sq ft
Foundation:	Crawl Space
Price Code:	H

Photographed home may have been modified from the original construction documents.

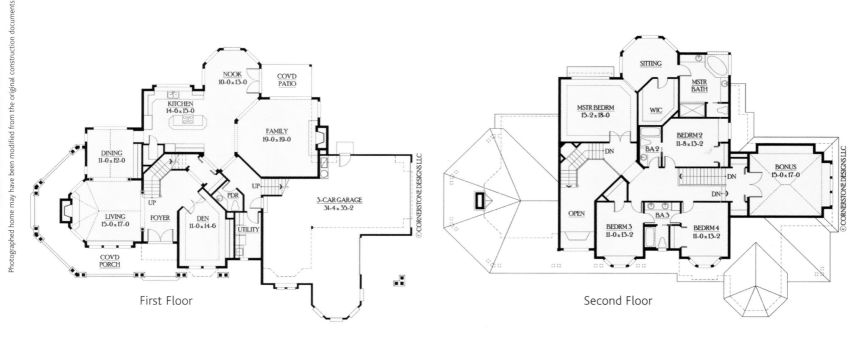

First Floor

Second Floor

© CORNERSTONE DESIGNS LLC

© CornerStone Designs, LLC.

Craftsman-style elegance defines this popular home. The front porch is perfect for a swing, while sheltering gable roofs highlight a dynamic façade composed of stone-based columns and shingle with bold trim. The floor plan works for today's lifestyle, with comfortable formal and family living areas featuring vaulted and coffered ceilings, columns and a covered BBQ patio.

Rockmore
CornerStone Designs
CHPCD01-M2535A3F-1
1-888-840-6020

Bedrooms:	3
Bath:	2-1/2
Width:	65'0"
Depth:	54'0"
1st Floor:	1450 sq ft
2nd Floor:	1470 sq ft
Living Area:	2920 sq ft
Foundation:	Crawl Space
Price Code:	F

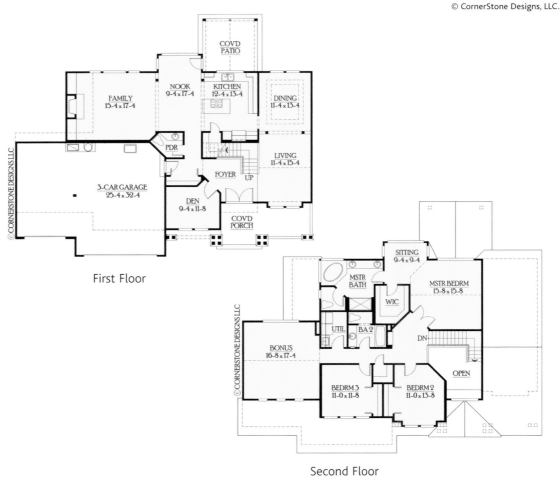

First Floor

Second Floor

Rear Elevation

© 1999 Donald A. Gardner, Inc.

This extraordinary four-bedroom estate features multiple gables with decorative wood brackets, arched windows and a stone and siding façade. Sharing the great room's cathedral ceiling, the loft makes an excellent reading nook. A sizable kitchen is open to a large gathering room for ultimate family togetherness.

Chesapeake

Donald A. Gardner Architects, Inc.
CHPDG01-783
1-888-840-6020

Bedrooms:	4
Bath:	3
Width:	99'8"
Depth:	78'8"
1st Floor:	3555 sq ft
2nd Floor:	250 sq ft
Total Living:	3805 sq ft
Bonus Room:	490 sq ft
Foundation:	Crawl Space*
Price Code:	H

*Other options available. See page 175.

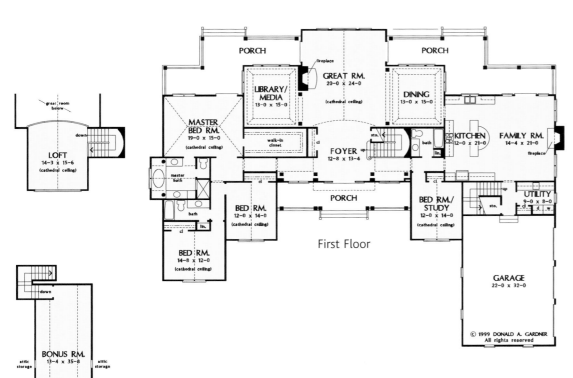

First Floor

Rear Elevation

A walkout basement makes this home perfect for hillsides, while its building materials and Craftsman details give it the look of a custom design. Interior columns and ceiling treatments create definition and distinction. The great room features a cathedral ceiling, fireplace, built-ins and access to the screened porch. The bonus room and storage area provide ample space for future use.

Gilchrist

Donald A. Gardner Architects, Inc.
CHPDG01-734-D
1-888-840-6020

Bedrooms:	4
Bath:	3-1/2
Width:	62'3"
Depth:	76'7"
1st Floor:	2094 sq ft
Basement Floor:	1038 sq ft
Total Living:	3132 sq ft
Bonus Room:	494 sq ft
Foundation:	Hillside Walkout
Price Code:	G

Rear Elevation

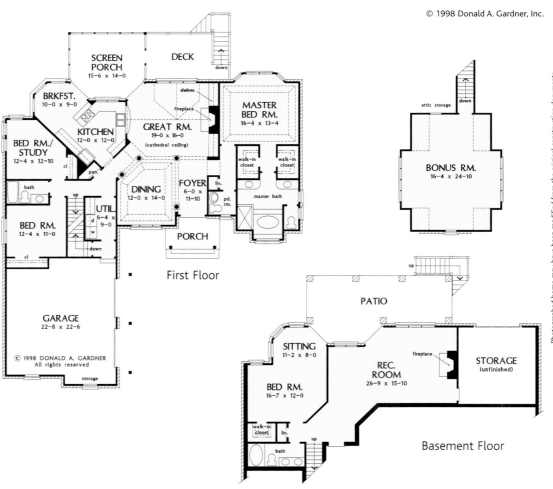

First Floor

Basement Floor

© The Sater Design Collection, Inc.

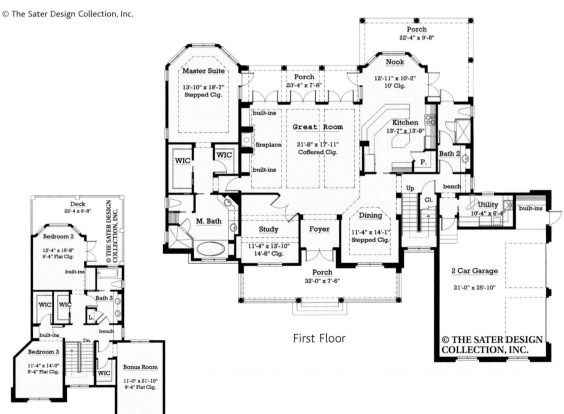

First Floor

Second Floor

© THE SATER DESIGN COLLECTION, INC.

Columns and coffered ceilings enlarge the interior spaces. The grand room features triple French doors, built-in cabinetry and a fireplace. The spacious kitchen boasts an eating bar, center work island, walk-in pantry and easy access to the dining room. Built-ins and walk-in closets complete two upstairs bedrooms. An over-the-garage bonus room houses a bath.

Nadine
The Sater Design Collection, Inc.
CHPDS01-7047
1-888-840-6020

Bedrooms:	3
Bath:	3
Width:	75'4"
Depth:	69'10"
1st Floor:	2215 sq ft
2nd Floor:	708 sq ft
Living Area:	2923 sq ft
Bonus Room:	420 sq ft
Foundation:	Crawl Space or Opt. Basement
Price Code:	G

Rear Elevation

HAWTHORNE
cornerstone designs, llc

Set off with stone and distinguished by dormers, columns, bays, shingles and trim, this Hampton-style beauty's façade is truly memorable.

The formal foyer, great hall, den, living room and dining room are guaranteed to impress visitors, while huge informal living areas comfort the family. The wraparound entry porch and rear BBQ porch provide ample opportunity for year-round outdoor living and entertaining.

The grand master suite with its huge closet and sitting room are reached from the formal foyer stair, while a convenient back stair connects the family room with remaining bedrooms and loft.

Above Right:
A visual feast of textures and materials, the kitchen's light-toned hardwood floors, tawny pecan cabinets and diagonal tile backsplash contrast dramatically with its forest green granite countertops. The expansive island doubles as a breakfast bar.

Right:
Two pairs of French doors opening to the front porch and windows that flank the cozy fireplace flood the living room with light. The painted mantel, wainscots, casings, coffers and crown moldings create a fresh and formal elegance.

Exteriors:
(Front) A majestic gable centers the *Hawthorne's* multi-featured façade, flanked by broad porches, delicate dormers and bold bays. The composition is both friendly and formal, with a delightful balance of elegant and eclectic elements.
(Rear) Perfect for a swing, a relaxing glass of iced tea or a family BBQ, a broad rear BBQ porch and a huge wraparound front porch connect the *Hawthorne* to the great outdoors.

© Cornerstone Designs, LLC.

Rear Elevation

CornerStone Designs, LLC

CHPCD01-M4720A3F-0
1-888-840-6020

Bedrooms:	4
Bath:	3-1/2
Width:	85'0"
Depth:	61'0"
1st Floor:	2240 sq ft
2nd Floor:	2480 sq ft
Living Area:	4720 sq ft
Foundation:	Crawl Space
Price Code:	I

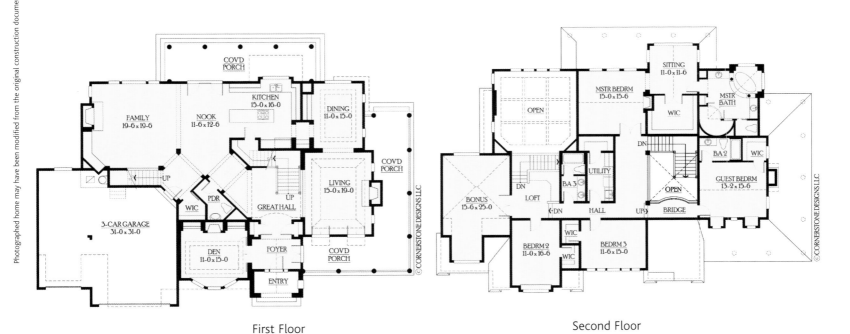

First Floor

Second Floor

DOGWOOD RIDGE
donald a. gardner architects, inc.

Influenced by Old-World artistry, this home defines and declares superior living, exemplifying the ultimate in style and grace.

Designed for a pristine wooded hillside, overlooking magnificent valley views, this home frames the mountains through a fanciful rear wall of windows. With a casually elegant floor plan and abundant outdoor living space, this home transforms everyday living into a fifty-two week vacation.

With its lush appointments and extraordinary emphasis on architectural detail, the *Dogwood Ridge* offers luxurious living for those who appreciate a masterwork of relaxation and refinement.

Above Right:
The breakfast counter performs dual roles, providing a place for quick meals and prep space.
Right:
Built-ins, wainscoting and a deep tray ceiling highlight the dining room.
Exteriors:
(Front) Stone and cedar shake give this home an Old-World look and feel.
(Rear) Covered porches and stone columns give the rear exterior drama and appeal that rivals the front façade.

© 2003 Allora, LLC.

Rear Elevation

Donald A. Gardner
Architects, Inc.
CHPAL01-5005
1-888-840-6020

Bedrooms:	3
Bath:	3-1/2
Width:	71'1"
Depth:	78'6"
1st Floor:	2090 sq ft
Basement:	1111 sq ft
Living Area:	3201 sq ft
Foundation:	Hillside Walkout
Price Code:	O

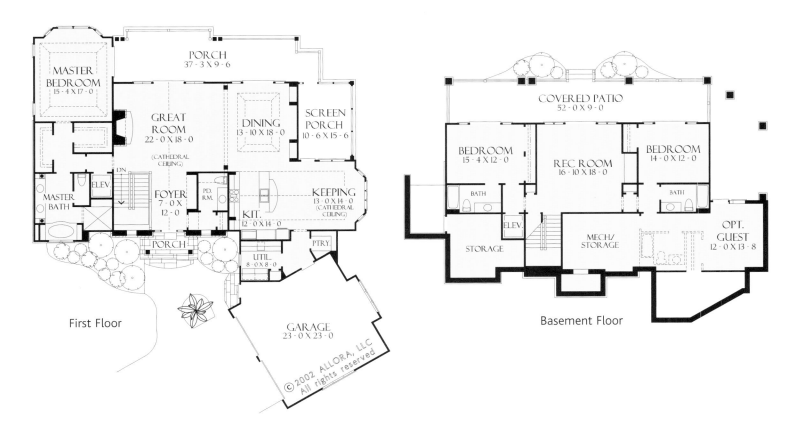

First Floor

MASTER BEDROOM 15-4 X 17-0

PORCH 37-3 X 9-6

GREAT ROOM 22-0 X 18-0 (CATHEDRAL CEILING)

DINING 13-10 X 18-0

SCREEN PORCH 10-6 X 15-6

DN

ELEV.

MASTER BATH

FOYER 7-0 X 12-0

PD. RM.

KIT. 12-0 X 14-0

KEEPING 13-0 X 14-0 (CATHEDRAL CEILING)

PORCH

UTIL. 8-0 X 8-0

PTRY.

GARAGE 23-0 X 23-0

Basement Floor

COVERED PATIO 52-0 X 9-0

BEDROOM 15-4 X 12-0

REC ROOM 16-10 X 18-0

BEDROOM 14-0 X 12-0

BATH

BATH

ELEV.

STORAGE

MECH/ STORAGE

OPT. GUEST 12-0 X 13-8

This Craftsman home takes advantage of hillside views with its deck, patio and abundance of rear windows. An open floor plan enhances the home's spaciousness. The great room features a cathedral ceiling, fireplace with built-ins and access to the generous rear deck. Designed for ultimate efficiency, the kitchen serves the great room, dining room and breakfast area with ease.

Heathridge

Donald A. Gardner Architects, Inc.
CHPDG01-763-D
1-888-840-6020

Bedrooms:	3
Bath:	3-1/2
Width:	72'4"
Depth:	66'0"
1st Floor:	2068 sq ft
Basement Floor:	930 sq ft
Total Living:	2998 sq ft
Foundation:	Hillside Walkout
Price Code:	F

Rear Elevation

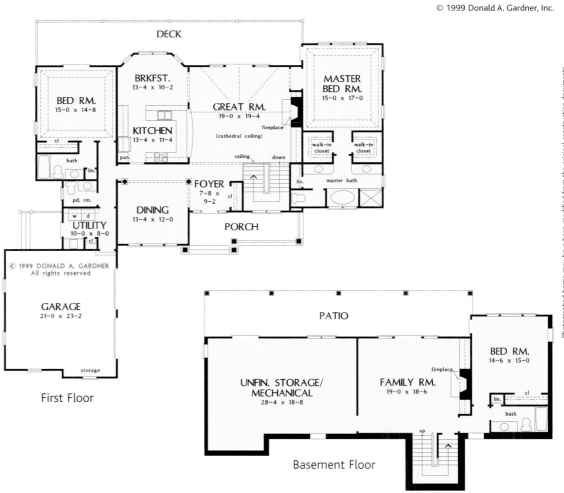

DECK

BED RM.
15-0 x 14-8

BRKFST.
13-4 x 10-2

GREAT RM.
19-0 x 19-4
(cathedral ceiling)

fireplace

MASTER BED RM.
15-0 x 17-0

walk-in closet

walk-in closet

KITCHEN
13-4 x 11-4

cl

bath

pan.

lin.

railing

down

master bath

lin.

FOYER
7-8 x 9-2

cl

pd. rm.

DINING
13-4 x 12-0

PORCH

UTILITY
10-0 x 8-0

w d

cl

GARAGE
21-0 x 23-2

storage

First Floor

PATIO

UNFIN. STORAGE/
MECHANICAL
28-4 x 18-8

FAMILY RM.
19-0 x 18-6

fireplace

BED RM.
14-6 x 15-0

lin.

cl

bath

up

Basement Floor

Photographed home may have been modified from the original construction documents.

© The Sater Design Collection, Inc.

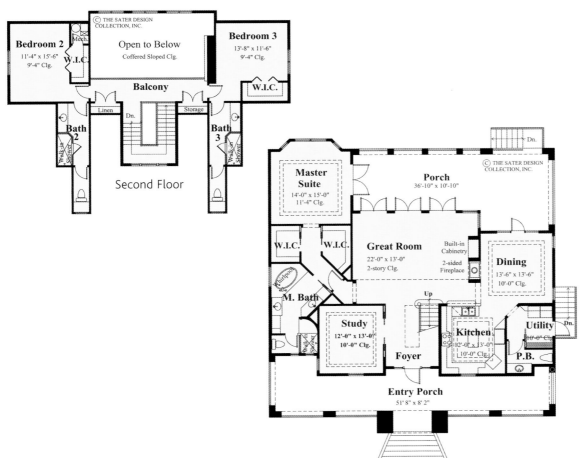

Second Floor

Bedroom 2
11'-4" x 15'-6"
9'-4" Clg.

© THE SATER DESIGN COLLECTION, INC.

Open to Below
Coffered Sloped Clg.

Bedroom 3
13'-8" x 11'-6"
9'-4" Clg.

W.I.C.

Balcony

W.I.C.

Bath 2

Linen

Dn.

Storage

Bath 3

First Floor

Master Suite
14'-0" x 15'-0"
11'-4" Clg.

Porch
36'-10" x 10'-10"

© THE SATER DESIGN COLLECTION, INC.

W.I.C.

W.I.C.

Great Room
22'-0" x 13'-0"
2-story Clg.

Built-in Cabinetry

2-sided Fireplace

Dining
13'-6" x 13'-6"
10'-0" Clg.

Whirlpool

M. Bath

Up

Study
12'-0" x 13'-0"
10'-0" Clg.

Foyer

Kitchen
12'-0" x 13'-0"
10'-0" Clg.

Utility
10'-0" Clg.

Dn.

P.B.

Entry Porch
51' 8" x 8' 2"

Mirrored dormers, a stone gable entry, classic columns and rustic balustrades garner attention from those who pass by. A coffered two-story sloped ceiling soars over the great room that features built-in cabinetry, French doors and easy access to the kitchen. To ensure privacy, the secondary bedrooms are placed on the upper floor away from the master suite and feature walk-in closets and private baths.

Stonebridge

The Sater Design Collection, Inc.
CHPDS01-6832
1-888-840-6020

Bedrooms:	3
Bath:	3
Width:	54'0"
Depth:	57'0"
1st Floor:	1798 sq ft
2nd Floor:	900 sq ft
Living Area:	2698 sq ft
Foundation:	Crawl Space
Price Code:	G

Rear Elevation

© The Sater Design Collection, Inc.

R ecessed arches and classic columns line the front porch. The bright, open floor plan is very inviting. Triple sliding glass doors connect the great room to the rear porch. The kitchen has a convenient pass-through, walk-in pantry and easy access to the formal dining room. The master retreat has a corner wall of glass bordering a whirlpool tub.

Sargent

The Sater Design Collection, Inc.
CHPDS01-7053
1-888-840-6020

Bedrooms:	3
Bath:	2
Width:	52'6"
Depth:	66'0"
1st Floor:	1487 sq ft
Living Area:	1487 sq ft
Foundation:	Crawl Space
Price Code:	D

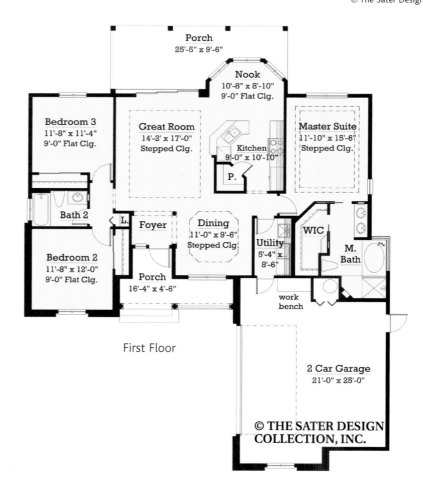

First Floor

© THE SATER DESIGN COLLECTION, INC.

Rear Elevation

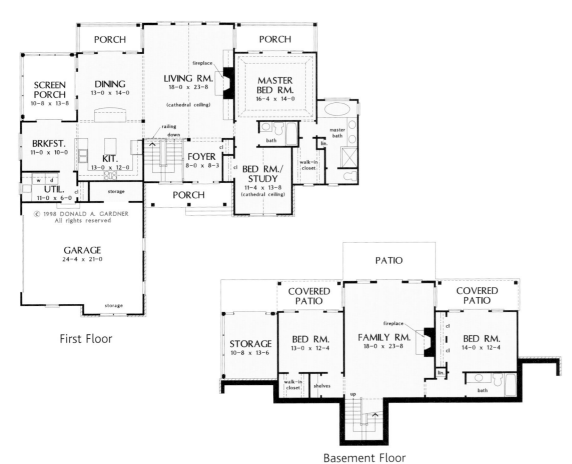

First Floor

PORCH

SCREEN PORCH
10-8 x 13-8

DINING
13-0 x 14-0

LIVING RM.
18-0 x 23-8
(cathedral ceiling)

fireplace

PORCH

MASTER BED RM.
16-4 x 14-0

master bath

walk-in closet

lin.

BRKFST.
11-0 x 10-0

KIT.
13-0 x 12-0

railing
down

FOYER
8-0 x 8-3

bath

cl

cl

BED RM./ STUDY
11-4 x 13-8
(cathedral ceiling)

UTIL.
11-0 x 6-0

w d

storage

cl

PORCH

© 1998 DONALD A. GARDNER
All rights reserved

GARAGE
24-4 x 21-0

storage

Basement Floor

PATIO

STORAGE
10-8 x 13-6

COVERED PATIO

BED RM.
13-0 x 12-4

FAMILY RM.
18-0 x 23-8

fireplace

COVERED PATIO

BED RM.
14-0 x 12-4

cl

cl

walk-in closet

shelves

up

lin.

bath

This walkout combines stucco, stone and cedar shakes for exceptional character. A dramatic cathedral ceiling heightens the open living room with central fireplace and built-ins. Porches flank the living room to allow its rear wall of windows uninterrupted views. Rear porches are entered through the dining room and master bedroom, while the breakfast and dining rooms enjoy screened porch access.

Vandenberg
Donald A. Gardner Architects, Inc.
CHPDG01-746-D
1-888-840-6020

Bedrooms:	4
Bath:	3
Width:	68'4"
Depth:	60'10"
1st Floor:	1810 sq ft
Basement Floor:	1146 sq ft
Total Living:	2956 sq ft
Foundation:	Hillside Walkout
Price Code:	F

Rear Elevation

A center dormer with arched window embellishes the exterior of this hillside walkout. The second-floor balcony overlooks the foyer and great room, while a back porch extends the great room. The master bedroom features porch access, a tray ceiling, walk-in and private bath. A bonus room resides over the three-car garage.

Peekskill

Donald A. Gardner Architects, Inc.

CHPDG01-780-D
1-888-840-6020

Bedrooms:	4
Bath:	3-1/2
Width:	81'4"
Depth:	68'8"
1st Floor:	1662 sq ft
2nd Floor:	585 sq ft
Basement Floor:	706 sq ft
Total Living:	2953 sq ft
Bonus Room:	575 sq ft
Foundation:	Hillside Walkout
Price Code:	F

Rear Elevation

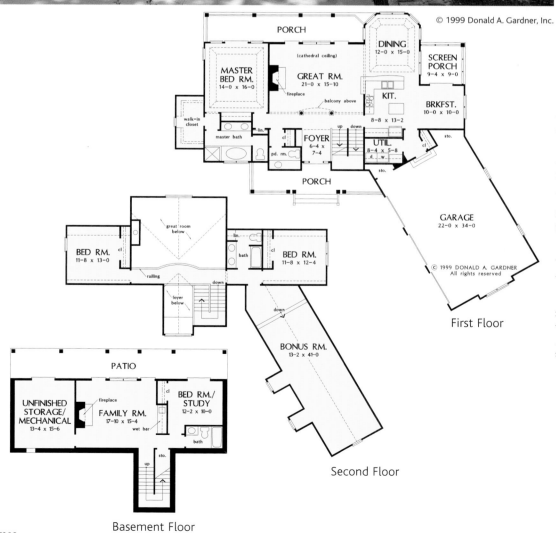

First Floor

Second Floor

Basement Floor

© The Sater Design Collection, Inc.

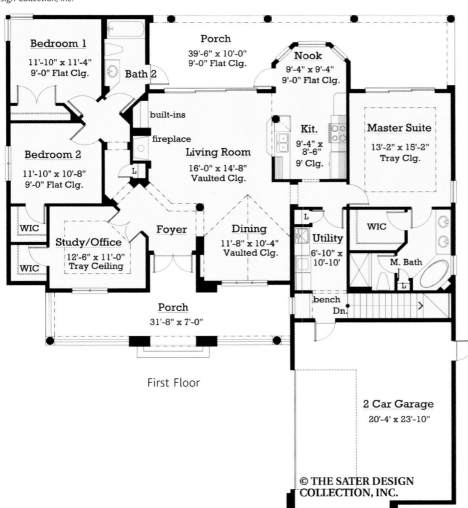

Bedroom 1
11'-10" x 11'-4"
9'-0" Flat Clg.

Bath 2

Porch
39'-6" x 10'-0"
9'-0" Flat Clg.

Nook
9'-4" x 9'-4"
9'-0" Flat Clg.

built-ins

fireplace

Kit.
9'-4" x
8'-6"
9' Clg.

Master Suite
13'-2" x 15'-2"
Tray Clg.

Bedroom 2
11'-10" x 10'-8"
9'-0" Flat Clg.

Living Room
16'-0" x 14'-8"
Vaulted Clg.

WIC

WIC

Study/Office
12'-6" x 11'-0"
Tray Ceiling

Foyer

Dining
11'-8" x 10'-4"
Vaulted Clg.

Utility
6'-10" x
10'-10'

WIC

M. Bath

WIC

bench
Dn.

Porch
31'-8" x 7'-0"

First Floor

2 Car Garage
20'-4' x 23'-10"

© THE SATER DESIGN COLLECTION, INC.

A Palladian window combines with multiple gables, decorative shutters and dormer windows to create a charming façade. The living room features built-in cabinetry, a fireplace and retreating glass doors granting views and access to the rear porch. The kitchen features a convenient pass-through and has easy access to the dining room and rear porch. A split-floor plan provides privacy to the master retreat and secondary bedrooms.

Chantel
The Sater Design Collection, Inc.
CHPDS01-7011
1-888-840-6020

Bedrooms: 3
Bath: 2
Width: 58'0"
Depth: 67'2"
1st Floor: 1822 sq ft
Living Area: 1822 sq ft
Foundation: Basement
Price Code: E

Rear Elevation

SOLSTICE SPRINGS

donald a. gardner architects, inc.

As the perfect meld between indoor and outdoor living, the *Solstice Springs* is a stunning blend of Craftsman exterior and a modern floor plan. Featuring sweeping gables, graceful arches over the garage door and front porch and a low-maintenance mixture of stone and siding, the *Solstice Springs* will make you never want to leave home.

Inside, exposed wooden beams run throughout the home and are instantly obvious in the foyer. Just as step away, the great room is nothing short of luxurious. A stunning fireplace creates a grand focal point, while the cathedral ceiling, French doors and built-in shelves showcase custom details.

The master suite is located on the first floor for both privacy and convenience. Including a sitting area and tray ceiling, the master bedroom encourages relaxation. Two walk-in closets, private privy, twin vanities and a separate shower and tub combination complete the suite. Downstairs, the basement includes a rec room and two bedrooms each with a full bath.

Above:
The kitchen's large center island is the perfect place for meal prep or quick, casual meals.
Right:
A spacious screen porch invites Mother Nature inside in a comfortable yet elegant manner.

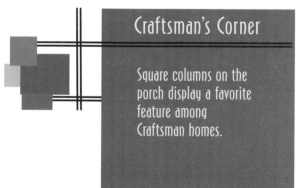

Craftsman's Corner

Square columns on the porch display a favorite feature among Craftsman homes.

Above:
The great room is not only open to the kitchen, but includes French doors and an abundance of windows to brighten the living space.

Right:
Accented by a bay window, the master bedroom also features a tray ceiling for additional luxury.

Exteriors:
(Front) A decorative bracket, shed dormer window, use of mixed materials and columns and arches elegantly combine to showcase irresistible Craftsman appeal.

Rear Elevation

Donald A. Gardner
Architects, Inc.
CHPAL01-5011
1-888-840-6020

Bedrooms:	3
Bath:	3-1/2
Width:	84'4"
Depth:	87'2"
1st Floor:	2207 sq ft
Basement:	1363 sq ft
Living Area:	3570 sq ft
Foundation:	Hillside Walkout
Price Code:	O

First Floor

Basement Floor

© 2000 Donald A. Gardner, Inc.

This stylish stone and stucco home features a partially finished walkout basement for sloping lots. The foyer is vaulted and includes a niche for displaying collectibles. The generous great room enjoys a dramatic cathedral ceiling, a rear wall of windows, access to two rear decks, a fireplace and built-in bookshelves.

MacLachlan

Donald A. Gardner Architects, Inc.

CHPDG01-825-D
1-888-840-6020

Bedrooms:	4
Bath:	3
Width:	64'0"
Depth:	62'4"
1st Floor:	1901 sq ft
Basement Floor:	1075 sq ft
Total Living:	2976 sq ft
Foundation:	Hillside Walkout
Price Code:	F

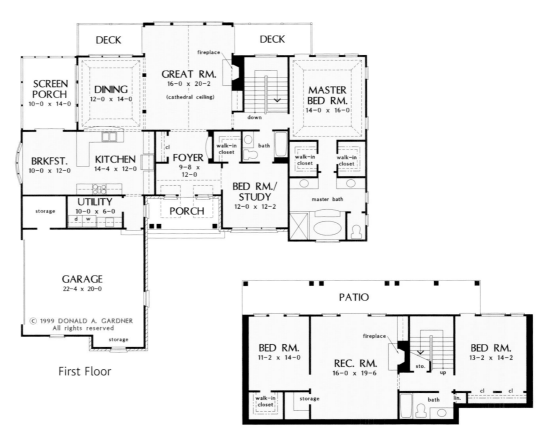

First Floor

Basement Floor

Rear Elevation

© 1999 Donald A. Gardner, Inc.

DECK

MASTER
BED RM.
15-0 x 13-4
(cathedral ceiling)

KITCHEN
10-0 x 13-4

(cathedral ceiling)

BED RM.
11-0 x 11-0

fireplace

GREAT RM.
16-0 x 17-0

walk-in
closet

cl

pan.

up

bath

cl

master
bath

d
w

FOYER
7-4 x
7-4

lin.

sto.

DINING
10-0 x 12-8

cl

BED RM.
11-0 x 11-0

cl

PORCH

attic
storage

down

attic
storage

BONUS RM.
12-0 x 20-0

GARAGE
21-0 x 20-0

storage

First Floor

Form and function blend together in this Arts and Crafts-style home. A bold combination of exterior building materials elicits interest outside, while inside, a practical design creates space in the home's economical floor plan. The foyer, great room, dining room and kitchen are completely open to one another. A cathedral ceiling vertically expands the great room and kitchen.

Tanglewood
Donald A. Gardner Architects, Inc.
CHPDG01-757
1-888-840-6020

Bedrooms:	3
Bath:	2
Width:	53'4"
Depth:	49'8"
1st Floor:	1473 sq ft
Total Living:	1473 sq ft
Bonus Room:	297 sq ft
Foundation:	Crawl Space*
Price Code:	C

*Other options available. See page 175.

Rear Elevation

TIMELESS AMERICAN HOMES

The Astoria; See page 170

Combining Craftsman flair with traditional features, these TIMELESS AMERICAN homes draw upon several styles to be at home in any neighborhood or rustic setting. Enjoying the look of shake, siding and stone, these plans utilize tried-and-true elements both on the exterior as well as the interior. Reflecting styles that enhance daily life, these homes never go out of style.

© 2002 Frank Betz Associates, Inc.

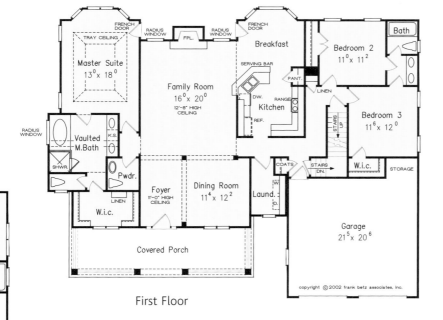

First Floor

First Floor labels:

TRAY CEILING · FRENCH DOOR · RADIUS WINDOW · FPL · RADIUS WINDOW · FRENCH DOOR · Breakfast · Bath

Master Suite 13⁰ x 18⁰

Family Room 16⁰ x 20⁰ 12'-8" HIGH CEILING

SERVING BAR · DW. · Kitchen · RANGE · REF. · PANT. · LINEN · LINEN

Bedroom 2 11⁰ x 11²

RADIUS WINDOW · Vaulted M.Bath · K.S. · SHWR. · Pwdr. · LINEN · W.i.c.

STAIRS UP · Bedroom 3 11⁶ x 12⁰

COATS · STAIRS DN. · W.i.c. · STORAGE

Foyer 11'-0" HIGH CEILING · Dining Room 11⁴ x 12² · Laund.

Garage 21⁵ x 20⁶

Covered Porch

copyright © 2002 frank betz associates, inc.

Opt. Second Floor labels:

Opt. W.i.c. · Optional Bedroom 4 11⁶ x 11⁷ · Opt. Bath

STAIRS DN. · OPEN RAIL

Opt. Bonus 11⁵ x 23³

Opt. Second Floor

Quaint…Timeless…Classic… all of these so accurately describe the charm that the *Guilford* exudes. From the cheery dormers, to the comfy front porch, to the board-and-batten shutters, this design stepped off the streets of yesteryear. Inside, the master suite features a wall of windows with views to the backyard. Two additional bedrooms share a divided bath.

Guilford

Frank Betz Associates, Inc.

CHPFB01-3689
1-888-840-6020

Bedrooms:	4
Bath:	3-1/2
Width:	62'0"
Depth:	50'0"
1st Floor:	1933 sq ft
Living Area:	1933 sq ft
Opt. 2nd Floor:	519 sq ft
Foundation:	Crawl Space or Basement
Price Code:	G

Rear Elevation

© 2002 Frank Betz Associates, Inc.

Shutters, native stone and shingles create the right mix of rugged and refined elements. A gallery foyer defined by arches and columns grants vistas that extend to the back of the property. Twin windows flank a centered fireplace in the family room. One wing of the home is dedicated to the owners' retreat, with a sitting area in the bedroom.

Montaigne

Frank Betz Associates, Inc.
CHPFB01-3731
1-888-840-6020

Bedrooms:	4
Bath:	3-1/2
Width:	62'4"
Depth:	50'0"
1st Floor:	1897 sq ft
2nd Floor:	1086 sq ft
Living Area:	2983 sq ft
Foundation:	Crawl Space or Basement
Price Code:	H

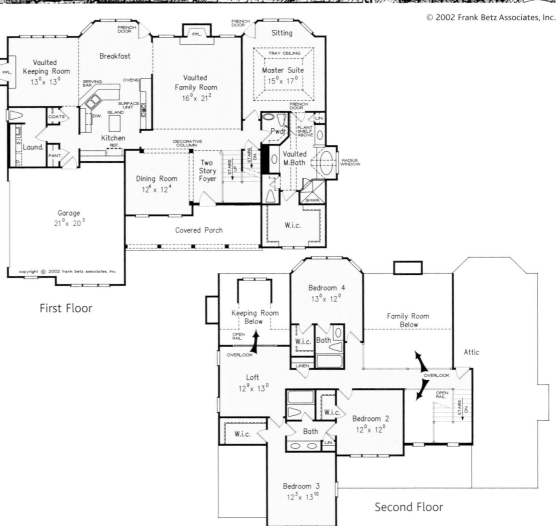

First Floor

Second Floor

Rear Elevation

© CornerStone Designs, LLC.

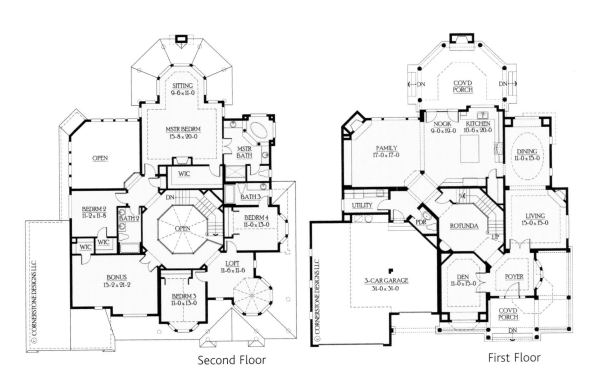

Second Floor

First Floor

Second Floor labels:
SITTING 9-6 x 11-0
MSTR BEDRM 15-8 x 20-0
MSTR BATH
OPEN
WIC
BEDRM 2 11-2 x 11-8
BATH 2
DN
OPEN
BATH 3
BEDRM 4 11-0 x 13-0
WIC
WIC
LOFT 11-6 x 11-6
BONUS 15-2 x 21-2
BEDRM 3 11-0 x 13-0
CORNERSTONE DESIGNS LLC

First Floor labels:
DN COVD PORCH DN
NOOK 9-0 x 19-0
KITCHEN 10-6 x 20-0
FAMILY 17-0 x 17-0
DINING 11-0 x 15-0
UTILITY
PDR
ROTUNDA
LIVING 15-0 x 15-0
UP
3-CAR GARAGE 31-0 x 31-0
DEN 11-0 x 15-0
FOYER
COVD PORCH
DN
CORNERSTONE DESIGNS LLC

A vision of Victorian elegance greets you, highlighted by the signature corner turret. From the columned wraparound entry porch to the traditional foyer accessing the formal rooms, a bold diagonal axis draws you through the dramatic two-story octagonal rotunda into the grand family room. Full of romance and packed with detail, the *Seaoria* is a grand modern expression of old-fashioned family living.

Seaoria
CornerStone Designs
CHPCD01-M4060A3F-5
1-888-840-6020

Bedrooms: 4
Bath: 3-1/2
Width: 65'0"
Depth: 80'0"
1st Floor: 2000 sq ft
2nd Floor: 2160 sq ft
Living Area: 4160 sq ft
Foundation: Crawl Space
Price Code: H

Rear Elevation

RYECROFT
donald a. gardner architects, inc.

Arched windows and arches in the covered front porch complement the gable peaks on the façade of this stylish Craftsman home.

Designed for sloping lots, this home positions its common living areas and master suite on the first floor and a generous recreation room and two family bedrooms on the lower level. A cathedral ceiling expands the foyer and great room, while the dining room and master bedroom and bath enjoy elegant tray ceilings. The island kitchen is open to the great room, dining room and breakfast area and features a nearby walk-in pantry.

Downstairs, two bedrooms and baths flank the recreation room with fireplace and wet bar.

Above Right:
Matching wooden cabinetry and appliances turn this kitchen into an instant gathering spot.
Right:
Built-in shelves and stylish transoms become elegant extras in the basement recreation room.
Exteriors:
(Front) Arches are abounding in the covered front porch and complement the gable peaks on the façade of this stylish Craftsman home with stone-and-siding exterior.
(Rear) The screen porch and covered patio provide more than ample space for outdoor entertaining.

Rear Elevation

Donald A. Gardner
Architects, Inc.
CHPDG01-824-D
1-888-840-6020

Bedrooms:	3
Bath:	3-1/2
Width:	59'0"
Depth:	59'4"
1st Floor:	1725 sq ft
Basement:	1090 sq ft
Living Area:	2815 sq ft
Foundation:	Hillside Walkout
Price Code:	F

First Floor

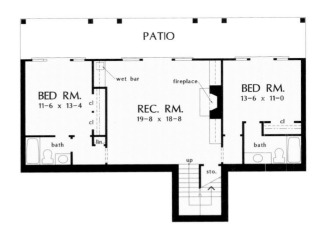

Basement Floor

The *Amelia's* façade is clean and simple, with a cozy front porch and gabled roofline. Upstairs, a loft is situated among the bedrooms making an ideal homework station or kids lounge. Optional bonus space is also available to be used as a possible fitness room or media center.

Amelia
Frank Betz Associates, Inc.
CHPFB01-3807
1-888-840-6020

Bedrooms:	4
Bath:	3
Width:	54'0"
Depth:	48'0"
1st Floor:	1663 sq ft
2nd Floor:	623 sq ft
Living Area:	2286 sq ft
Bonus Room:	211 sq ft
Foundation:	Crawl Space or Basement
Price Code:	H

First Floor

Second Floor

Rear Elevation

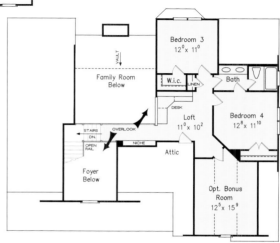

© 2005 Frank Betz Associates, Inc.

First Floor

Opt. Second Floor

The plaza entry with brick, stone and vertical siding fits into any neighborhood. The vaulted foyer opens up to a grand room with coffered ceilings. A guest suite offers visitors a private bath. Two secondary bedrooms occupy one wing of the home, while the optional bonus room on the second floor gives homeowners room to grow.

Barton Creek
Frank Betz Associates, Inc.
CHPFB01-3928
1-888-840-6020

Bedrooms:	4
Bath:	4-1/2
Width:	65'0"
Depth:	75'4"
1st Floor:	2699 sq ft
Living Area:	2699 sq ft
Opt. 2nd Floor:	418 sq ft
Foundation:	Slab, Crawl Space or Basement
Price Code:	H

Rear Elevation

The high-beamed tray ceiling of the master suite makes the *Keenes Point* the perfect home for a mountain or lake home. A rear deck off the kitchen makes entertaining fun and convenient. A suite on the main level offers guests access to a private bath and walk-in closet.

Keenes Pointe

Frank Betz Associates, Inc.
CHPFB01-3940
1-888-840-6020

Bedrooms:	5
Bath:	4
Width:	54'0"
Depth:	70'4"
1st Floor:	1895 sq ft
2nd Floor:	963 sq ft
Living Area:	2858 sq ft
Bonus Room:	352 sq ft
Foundation:	Crawl Space or Basement
Price Code:	H

Rear Elevation

Second Floor

First Floor

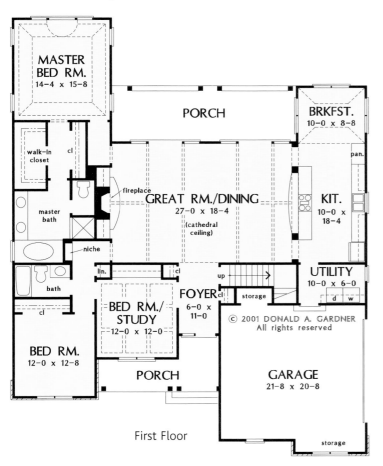

First Floor

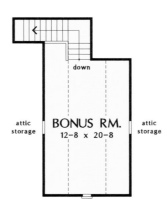

Mix a little Europe with Arts and Crafts and this design is the outcome. The mix of exterior materials complement the interior features like the cathedral ceiling with striking exposed beams, French doors accessing the rear porch and built-ins flanking the fireplace. A coffered ceiling details the flexible bedroom/study, while a vaulted ceiling crowns the breakfast area. Columns mark the kitchen pass-through.

Edinburgh

Donald A. Gardner Architects, Inc.
CHPDG01-914
1-888-840-6020

Bedrooms:	3
Bath:	2
Width:	53'4"
Depth:	67'8"
1st Floor:	1983 sq ft
Total Living:	1983 sq ft
Bonus Room:	341 sq ft
Foundation:	Crawl Space*
Price Code:	D

*Other options available. See page 175.

Rear Elevation

JERIVALE

donald a. gardner architects, inc.

Using materials that combine the rugged frontier with stately elegance, this exterior has a grand, majestic façade. Four towering columns frame the dramatic barrel-vault entrance, while clerestories mimic the arched theme. Cedar shake, stone and siding complement a metal roof over the front porch.

The two-story foyer has impressive views of the study, dining room, living room and balcony. Cathedral ceilings top the family room and master bedroom, while a vaulted ceiling tops the living room. Built-ins, three fireplaces and a walk-in pantry add special touches.

Every bedroom has walk-in closets, while the master bedroom's sitting area, upstairs library and versatile bonus room round out a home that is large on living and luxury.

Above:
Pendant lights and copious windows illuminate the chef-friendly kitchen that overlooks the breakfast and family rooms.
Right:
Overflowing with custom details, the living room boasts a soaring cathedral ceiling and built-in shelves that flank the stunning fireplace.

Craftsman's Corner

The deep porch, square columns and use of mixed materials grants a timeless finish to this home's façade.

Above and Right:
Choosing to add a basement lounge, this homeowner created the ideal place to entertain. The basement bar includes ample seating, fine masonry and rich detail , and the home theater's ceiling treatment and impressive wood detailing add drama and luxury to this lower-level oasis.

Exteriors:
(Front) Stone and siding coupled with multiple columns and an arched portico blend for immediate curb appeal in this Craftsman home.
(Rear) The sprawling rear exterior includes not-one-but-two screen porches, in addition to a patio, to create the ultimate outdoor entertaining space.

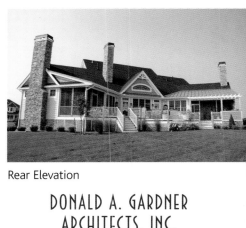

Rear Elevation

DONALD A. GARDNER ARCHITECTS, INC.

CHPDG01-1033-A

1-888-840-6020

Bedrooms:	3
Bath:	3-1/2
Width:	92'5"
Depth:	71'10"
1st Floor:	2766 sq ft
2nd Floor:	881 sq ft
Living Area:	3647 sq ft
Bonus:	407 sq ft
*Opt. Basement:	2780 sq ft
Foundation:	Basement or Crawl Space
Price Code:	H

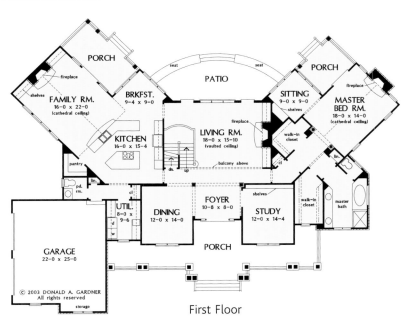

First Floor

Second Floor

Optional Basement Floor

* Note: Basement floor plan not to scale.
Basement Plan Price Schedule : 1 Set = $1,050, 4 Set = $1,100, 8 Set = $1,160, Vellum = $1,410

© 2002 Frank Betz Associates, Inc.

This design was created to give homeowners living spaces that are supplementary to the traditional rooms found in most plans. The master bedroom is enhanced by a private sitting area with views overlooking the backyard. Just off the breakfast area is a bright and sunny keeping room with a radius window.

Oak Knoll

Frank Betz Associates, Inc.
CHPFB01-3734
1-888-840-6020

Bedrooms:	4
Bath:	3
Width:	57'0"
Depth:	53'6"
1st Floor:	1894 sq ft
2nd Floor:	683 sq ft
Living Area:	2577 sq ft
Bonus Room:	210 sq ft
Foundation:	Crawl Space or Basement
Price Code:	H

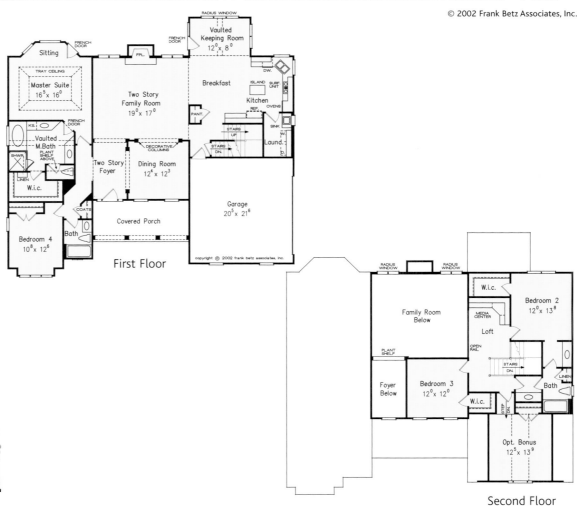

First Floor

Second Floor

Rear Elevation

© CornerStone Designs, LLC.

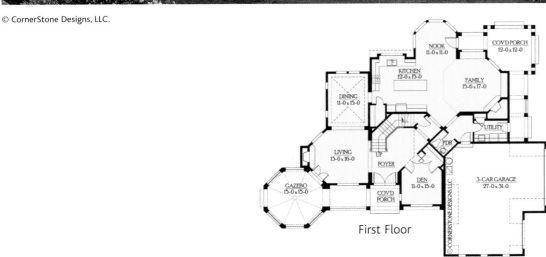

First Floor

Labels within First Floor:
- NOOK 11-0 x 11-0
- COVD PORCH 12-0 x 12-0
- KITCHEN 12-0 x 15-0
- FAMILY 15-6 x 17-0
- DINING 11-0 x 15-0
- UTILITY
- LIVING 15-0 x 16-0
- PDR
- UP
- FOYER
- DEN 11-0 x 15-0
- 3-CAR GARAGE 27-0 x 31-0
- GAZEBO 15-0 x 15-0
- COVD PORCH

Second Floor

Labels within Second Floor:
- SITTING 11-0 x 11-0
- MSTR BEDRM 13-6 x 17-2
- WIC
- MSTR BATH
- BEDRM 2 11-2 x 11-4
- DN
- BA 2
- WIC
- OPEN
- LANDING
- HALL
- WIC
- OPEN
- BEDRM 3 11-0 x 14-2
- WIC
- BA 3
- BEDRM 4 11-0 x 11-6
- BONUS 13-0 x 17-6

This grand Hampton estate creates a feeling of warmth and elegance while providing every modern convenience. The formal rooms and family spaces are connected to the outdoors with generous front and rear covered porches, providing great versatility for entertaining. The grand stair leads to the luxurious master suite with its octagonal sitting room, offering privacy from the bonus room and three secondary bedrooms.

Bayview
CornerStone Designs
CHPCD01-M3590B3S-0
1-888-840-6020

Bedrooms:	4
Bath:	3-1/2
Width:	77'0"
Depth:	66'6"
1st Floor:	1761 sq ft
2nd Floor:	1831 sq ft
Living Area:	3592 sq ft
Foundation:	Crawl Space
Price Code:	H

Rear Elevation

© The Sater Design Collection, Inc.

Two-arch top dormers canopied by a central gable with matchstick detailing adorn the façade. Built-ins, a fireplace and a two-story coffered ceiling enhance the great room. The kitchen has a convenient pass-through to the great room, close access to the dining room, a center work island and a butler's pantry. The master suite features a private porch, luxe bath and a walk-in closet.

Meadowsbrook

The Sater Design Collection, Inc.

CHPDS01-7042
1-888-840-6020

Bedrooms:	3
Bath:	2-1/2
Width:	70'0"
Depth:	55'8"
1st Floor:	1493 sq ft
2nd Floor:	676 sq ft
Living Area:	2169 sq ft
Foundation:	Crawl Space or Opt. Basement
Price Code:	F

Rear Elevation

First Floor

Second Floor

First Floor

Bedroom 2
15⁰ x 11⁰

Bath

Bedroom 3
12⁵ x 11⁰

Bath

Bdrm. 4/
Office
12⁷ x 11⁰

Foyer
10'-0" HIGH
CEILING

Dining Room
12⁵ x 12⁰
10'-0" HIGH
CEILING

Covered Porch

FRENCH
DOOR

RADIUS
TRANSOM

Breakfast

DESK

TRAY CEILING

Master Suite
13⁸ x 18⁶

SERVING BAR

Vaulted
Family Room
15³ x 21⁸
17'-3" HIGH CEILING

FPL.

BUILT-IN
CABINETS

VAULT

VAULT

Kitchen

DW.

REF.

RANGE

PANT.

FRENCH
DOOR

COATS

Laund.

LINEN

W.i.c.

KS.

Vaulted
M.Bath

SHWR.

RADIUS
WINDOW

DECORATIVE
COLUMNS

STAIRS
UP

STAIRS
DN

Garage
21⁰ x 21³

copyright © 2003 frank betz associates, inc.

Opt. Second Floor

STAIRS
DN

Opt. Bonus
Room
11⁰ x 19²

S hutters, shingles and siding wrap the familiar Colonial lines of this country cottage with a sweet disposition. At the heart of the home, built-in cabinetry and a hearth create an ambience that is right at home with the scenery. An office suite provides an ideal arrangement for a guest room.

Lincoln Park
Frank Betz Associates, Inc.
CHPFB01-3795
1-888-840-6020

Bedrooms:	4
Bath:	3
Width:	57'0"
Depth:	66'0"
1st Floor:	2211 sq ft
Living Area:	2211 sq ft
Opt. 2nd Floor:	227 sq ft
Foundation:	Slab, Crawl Space or Basement
Price Code:	H

Rear Elevation

SWEETWATER
frank betz associates, inc.

A street-friendly façade and flexible floor plan create an easygoing style that prevails throughout this livable design. Rich with period details, this new classic home integrates sophisticated amenities with a relaxed spirit that invites impromptu family gatherings. A sheltered entry and front covered porch lead to the two-story foyer, creating a grand introduction to the spacious interior. A planning desk is thoughtfully placed near the breakfast nook, and a wall of glass permits sunlight to pour in and brighten the room. The upper level provides a spectacular master suite with a vaulted bath and walk-in closet, knee space vanity and a windowed tub.

Above Right:
A unique moss-green stain adds interest to the mantel and bookshelf.
Right:
The spacious master suite allows the homeowner plenty of room to create a retreat.
Exterior:
(Front) Clapboard siding and rugged fieldstone evoke the charm of simpler time.

Rear Elevation

Frank Betz Associates, Inc.

CHPFB01-3691
1-888-840-6020

Bedrooms:	4
Bath:	3
Width:	54'4"
Depth:	36'0"
1st Floor:	1164 sq ft
2nd Floor:	916 sq ft
Living Area:	2080 sq ft
Foundation:	Crawl Space or Basement
Price Code:	F

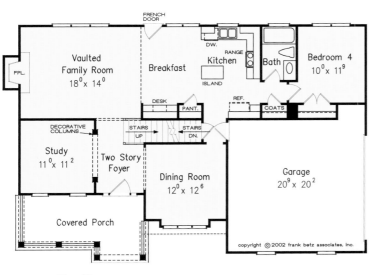

First Floor

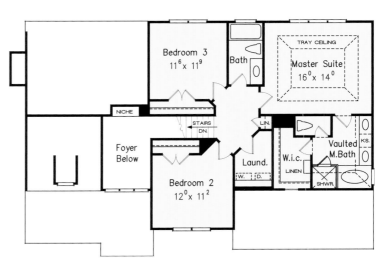

Second Floor

Willow Creek's inviting exterior combines an attractive combination of stone and siding, graced by a columned front porch. The kitchen is conveniently linked to a large laundry room. One wing of the home is dedicated solely to the master suite with an elegant tray ceiling and a large window for rear views.

Willow Creek

Frank Betz Associates, Inc.

CHPFB01-3539
1-888-840-6020

Bedrooms:	3
Bath:	2-1/2
Width:	52'4"
Depth:	46'10"
1st Floor:	1399 sq ft
2nd Floor:	576 sq ft
Living Area:	1975 sq ft
Bonus Room:	221 sq ft
Foundation:	Slab, Crawl Space or Basement
Price Code:	H

First Floor

First floor rooms: master bedroom 13' x 16'; family room 18'2" x 15'8"; breakfast 12'2" x 10'2"; kitchen 11'10" x 11'2"; dining 11'6" x 12'; garage 20' x 21'0"; foyer; covered porch; up; dn.

copyright © 2000 frank betz associates, inc.

Second Floor

Second floor rooms: family room below; bedroom 12'0" x 11'6"; foyer below; bedroom 11'6" x 12'0"; computer nook; opt. bonus room 12'0" x 15'2"; dn.

Rear Elevation

From the exclusive

Southern Living

Design Collection

© The Sater Design Collection, Inc.

First Floor

Porch

Nook
10'-4" x 7'-7"

Great Room
16'-4" x 17'-10"
Coffered Clg.

Master Suite
13'-0" x 16'-2"
Tray Clg.

Bedroom 2
12'-0" x 13'-4"

CL

workbench

Garage
18'-0" x 23'-0"

fireplace

built-in

CL

Kitchen
10'-2" x 11'-10"

Up

L

Her
WIC

© THE SATER DESIGN
COLLECTION, INC.

His
WIC

Bedroom 1
12'-0" x 11'-0"

L

Bath

Foyer

Dining
13'-10" x 11'-4"
Stepped Clg.

L

M.
Bath

Utility

CL

P

Porch

Bonus Room
16'-6" x 11'-0"

Bath

© THE SATER DESIGN
COLLECTION, INC.

Dn

Second Floor

Built-in cabinetry, a cozy fireplace, coffered ceiling and French doors to the back porch make the great room the heart of the home. The kitchen has a convenient pass-through to the great room, close access to the dining room, a center work island and a walk-in pantry. A split-floor plan allows privacy for the master suite located on one side of the home and the secondary bedrooms located on the other.

Saville

The Sater Design Collection, Inc.

CHPDS01-7045
1-888-840-6020

Bedrooms:	3
Bath:	2
Width:	81'0"
Depth:	50'0"
1st Floor:	1989 sq ft
Living Area:	1989 sq ft
Bonus Room:	274 sq ft
Foundation:	Crawl Space or Opt. Basement
Price Code:	E

Rear Elevation

© CornerStone Designs, LLC.

Strong shingle-style details create a timeless exterior with a rustic flavor. The front porch is highlighted by bold columns with stone bases, heavy brackets and contrasting trim. The floor plan's open family areas complement the formal dining room and den. Upstairs, the large bonus room separates the private master suite from the secondary bedrooms and laundry.

Summit

CornerStone Designs

CHPCD01-M2795A2FU-0
1-888-840-6020

Bedrooms:	3
Bath:	2-1/2
Width:	32'0"
Depth:	54'0"
1st Floor:	1405 sq ft
2nd Floor:	1348 sq ft
Lower Level:	42 sq ft
Living Area:	2795 sq ft
Foundation:	Crawl Space
Price Code:	F

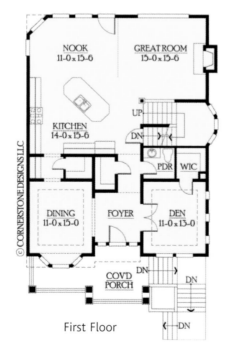

First Floor

NOOK 11-0 x 15-6

GREAT ROOM 15-0 x 15-6

KITCHEN 14-0 x 15-6

UP
DN
PDR WIC

DINING 11-0 x 15-0

FOYER

DEN 11-0 x 13-0

COVD PORCH
DN
DN
DN

© CORNERSTONE DESIGNS LLC

Second Floor

MSTR BATH
WIC
MSTR BEDRM 15-2 x 15-6

BONUS 15-0 x 16-0
DN
BA 2

BEDRM 3 11-0 x 13-2
UTILITY
BEDRM 2 11-2 x 11-2

© CORNERSTONE DESIGNS LLC

Lower Level

CRAWL SPACE
UP
UP

2-CAR GARAGE 20-10 x 27-6
SHOP 9-10 x 18-10

UP
UP

© CORNERSTONE DESIGNS LLC

Rear Elevation

© CornerStone Designs, LLC.

A whimsical gambrel and square turret highlight a façade full of curb appeal. Stone, shingle siding and shutters combine to create a lively composition. The soaring foyer and formal rooms lead to the open family area, covered BBQ patio and den. Upstairs finds the vaulted master suite plus three bedrooms, laundry and large bonus room.

Sycamore
CornerStone Designs
CHPCD01-M2780A3F-0
1-888-840-6020

Bedrooms:	4
Bath:	2-1/2
Width:	40'0"
Depth:	60'0"
1st Floor:	1330 sq ft
2nd Floor:	1450 sq ft
Living Area:	2780 sq ft
Foundation:	Crawl Space
Price Code:	F

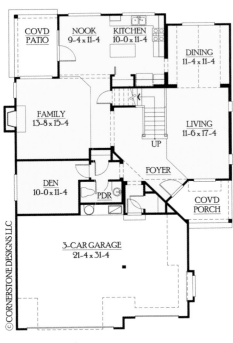

First Floor

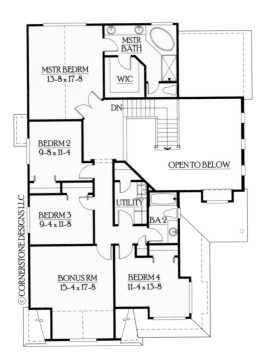

Second Floor

Rear Elevation

© 2002 Donald A. Gardner, Inc.

This cottage combines stone and siding for a striking façade. A box-bay window is capped with a metal roof, while the front-entry garage adds convenience. Decorative ceiling treatments enhance the great room, dining room, master bedroom and the bedroom/study. The bonus room, which is accessible from the foyer, provides space for a home office, gym or media room.

Irby

Donald A. Gardner Architects, Inc.

CHPDG01-993

1-888-840-6020

Bedrooms:	3
Bath:	2
Width:	55'6"
Depth:	46'0"
1st Floor:	1580 sq ft
Total Living:	1580 sq ft
Bonus Room:	367 sq ft
Foundation:	Crawl Space*
Price Code:	D

*Other options available. See page 175.

Rear Elevation

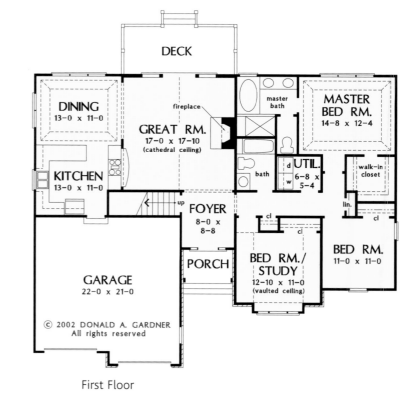

BONUS RM.
14-6 x 21-0

attic storage

attic storage

down

DECK

DINING
13-0 x 11-0

GREAT RM.
17-0 x 17-10
(cathedral ceiling)

fireplace

master bath

MASTER BED RM.
14-8 x 12-4

KITCHEN
13-0 x 11-0

bath

UTIL.
6-8 x 5-4

walk-in closet

lin.

cl

FOYER
8-0 x 8-8

up

GARAGE
22-0 x 21-0

PORCH

BED RM./STUDY
12-10 x 11-0
(vaulted ceiling)

cl

cl

BED RM.
11-0 x 11-0

cl

First Floor

An Arts and Crafts façade boasts elegant curb appeal as double dormers echo the dual-arched portico. Twin sets of tapered columns provide architectural detail in this lavish exterior. The master bedroom is flanked by a large, rear porch that creates additional space to entertain guests or enjoy Mother Nature. A vaulted ceiling, dual sinks and walk-in closets give the master suite additional flair.

Summerhill

Donald A. Gardner Architects, Inc.
CHPDG01-1090
1-888-840-6020

Bedrooms:	3
Bath:	2
Width:	56'4"
Depth:	73'0"
1st Floor:	2193 sq ft
Total Living:	2193 sq ft
Bonus Room:	387 sq ft
Foundation:	Crawl Space*
Price Code:	E

*Other options available. See page 175.

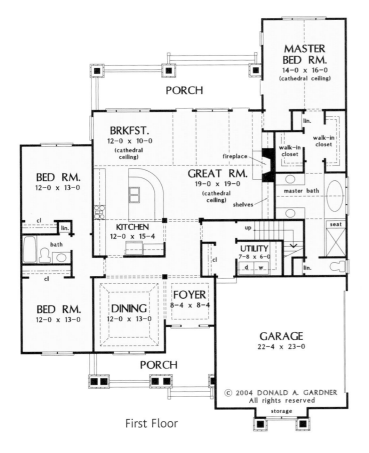

First Floor

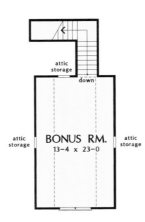

Rear Elevation

HAZELWOOD
cornerstone designs, llc

The *Hazelwood* brings country charm to the city or contemporary elegance to the country. Its wraparound entry porch, stone-accented columns, gables, bays and brackets convey a comfortable sense of home.

The den located at the entry works well for a home office. The island kitchen, bayed nook and grand family room create an open, flexible family living area.

A dramatic bridge at the top of the stairwell spans the spectacular two-story volumes of the central hall and family room, providing access and privacy for the deluxe master suite. The children's wing includes two bedrooms, a bath and bonus room.

Above Right:
Cherry-stained hardwood floors and cabinets, stainless-steel appliances, and tawny marble counter and backsplashes give the chef's kitchen a sensuous atmosphere. The center kitchen island provides seating while the matching butler's pantry connects to the dining room.

Far Right:
A soaring stone fireplace with a massive, dark-stained wood mantel and wood storage below highlights the grand family room. High windows bring in extra light and allow views of the woods beyond.

Right:
Oversize newel posts anchor the classic Craftsman details of the central stairwell. Bold columns and ceiling coffers define the bridge and hallway above.

Exteriors:
(*Front*) Combining timeless forms for a fresh feeling, the *Hazelwood*'s mix of Craftsman and farmhouse features create a friendly and inviting façade.
(*Rear*) A broad expanse of family room and nook windows face the rear, bringing in natural light while providing easy access to the patio and back yard.

© CornerStone Designs, LLC

Rear Elevation

CornerStone Designs, LLC

CHPCD01-M3130A3S-0
1-888-840-6020

Bedrooms:	3
Bath:	2-1/2
Width:	59'0"
Depth:	50'0"
1st Floor:	1630 sq ft
2nd Floor:	1500 sq ft
Living Area:	3130 sq ft
Foundation:	Crawl Space
Price Code:	F

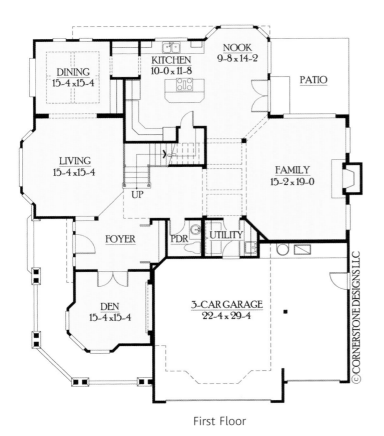

First Floor

DINING 15-4 x 15-4
KITCHEN 10-0 x 11-8
NOOK 9-8 x 14-2
PATIO
LIVING 15-4 x 15-4
FAMILY 15-2 x 19-0
UP
FOYER
PDR
UTILITY
DEN 15-4 x 15-4
3-CAR GARAGE 22-4 x 29-4

© CORNERSTONE DESIGNS LLC

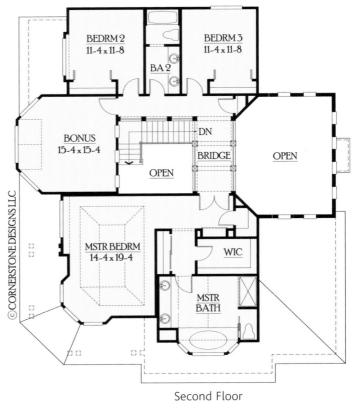

Second Floor

BEDRM 2 11-4 x 11-8
BEDRM 3 11-4 x 11-8
BA 2
BONUS 15-4 x 15-4
DN
BRIDGE
OPEN
OPEN
MSTR BEDRM 14-4 x 19-4
WIC
MSTR BATH

© CORNERSTONE DESIGNS LLC

© 1998 Donald A. Gardner, Inc.

Custom details accent this stone and wood siding home, designed with numerous windows to maximize exterior views. Inside, this home is remarkably open. Visually, the great room, dining room, kitchen, breakfast area and loft flow effortlessly together. The master bedroom features a tray ceiling and a trio of bayed windows capped by a circular clerestory.

Avalon

Donald A. Gardner Architects, Inc.

CHPDG01-726
1-888-840-6020

Bedrooms:	3
Bath:	2-1/2
Width:	84'10"
Depth:	60'0"
1st Floor:	1896 sq ft
2nd Floor:	692 sq ft
Total Living:	2588 sq ft
Foundation:	Crawl Space*
Price Code:	F

*Other options available. See page 175.

Rear Elevation

STORAGE
12-0 x 8-10

GARAGE
22-0 x 22-0

UTILITY

storage

pd. rm.

cl

w d

DECK

BRKFST.
9-8 x 13-0

KITCHEN
11-0 x 13-2

pan.

STUDY
11-0 x 13-0

master bath

walk-in closet

DINING
11-0 x 17-4

(cathedral ceiling)

GREAT RM.
22-0 x 18-0

(cathedral ceiling)

fireplace

up

MASTER BED RM.
15-0 x 17-10

PORCH

First Floor

STORAGE
11-4 x 15-8

attic storage

attic storage

BED RM.
11-4 x 12-8

attic storage

cl

BED RM.
13-0 x 13-0

lin.

bath

skylight

cl

up   up

down

LOFT/STUDY
12-0 x 13-0

attic storage

dining room below

great room below

Second Floor

© 2004 Frank Betz Associates, Inc.

A furniture niche in the foyer creates a place for that special piece that will make an attractive first impression. Coffered ceilings and built-in cabinetry in the family room make this room the natural center-point of the home. A vaulted keeping room adjoins the kitchen area, providing an additional cozy gathering spot.

Stoney River

Frank Betz Associates, Inc.

CHPFB01-3866
1-888-840-6020

Bedrooms:	3
Bath:	3-1/2
Width:	65'4"
Depth:	85'6"
1st Floor:	2876 sq ft
Living Area:	2876 sq ft
Opt. 2nd Floor:	393 sq ft
Foundation:	Crawl Space or Basement
Price Code:	H

First Floor

Opt. Second Floor

Rear Elevation

© CornerStone Designs, LLC.

Hampton-style elegance abounds in this dramatic residence. The sculptured façade is a stunning composition of stone, shingles, shutters, columns, bold arches and trim details. The family friendly floor plan provides generous formal and informal living spaces and a private den downstairs along with a luxury master suite, three secondary bedrooms and laundry room upstairs.

Canyon Creek
CornerStone Designs
CHPCD01-M2400C3F-0
1-888-840-6020

Bedrooms:	4
Bath:	2-1/2
Width:	62'0"
Depth:	42'0"
1st Floor:	1230 sq ft
2nd Floor:	1190 sq ft
Living Area:	2420 sq ft
Foundation:	Crawl Space
Price Code:	E

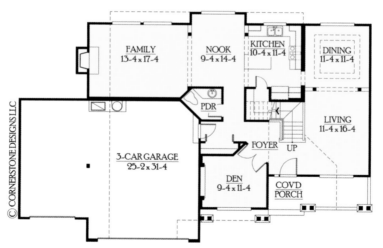

First Floor

Second Floor

Rear Elevation

© 2004 Frank Betz Associates, Inc.

First Floor

Vaulted Keeping Room 14⁰ x 14⁰
Breakfast
Vaulted Family Room 19⁰ x 17⁰
Master Suite 17⁰ x 17⁰
Sitting Area
Laund.
Kitchen
Mud Room
Dining Room 13⁹ x 12²
Foyer
Vaulted M.Bath
Vaulted Guest Room 12⁰ x 13⁰
Garage 21⁵ x 21¹⁰
Covered Porch

Second Floor

Bedroom 3 11⁹ x 15⁰
Bath
Bedroom 2 13⁰ x 14⁰
Teen Suite 20⁴ x 16²
Attic

Fieldstone accents against board-and-batten siding generate the welcoming and warm appeal that traditional homes are known for. A vaulted keeping room connects to the kitchen and breakfast areas, creating that relaxing place to rest and unwind. A teen suite upstairs is equipped with a built-in desk, making this spot the perfect homework station and hang-out spot.

McGinnis Ferry
Frank Betz Associates, Inc.
CHPFB01-3879
1-888-840-6020

Bedrooms: 4
Bath: 3
Width: 65'4"
Depth: 53'8"
1st Floor: 2224 sq ft
2nd Floor: 1030 sq ft
Living Area: 3254 sq ft
Foundation: Crawl Space or Basement
Price Code: I

Rear Elevation

HOPKINS
frank betz associates, inc.

A welcoming front porch draws inspiration from nostalgic homes of yesteryear, and a charming mixture of brick and siding blend to merge country and traditional styles on the *Hopkins*. A vaulted ceiling in the living room as well as two-story ceilings in the foyer and family room enhance and expand visual space, making rooms appear larger while allowing them to retain their intimacy. The traffic flow is well thought out and incredibly efficient for busy lifestyles, providing all the amenities today's families desire. A French door conveniently located in the kitchen allows easy access for outdoor activities. Large windows bring light and outdoor views into the home.

Above Right:
A decorative ceiling, glass shower and garden tub pamper the owners with style and space.

Right:
The warm-colored cabinetry and green tile backsplash echo the colors of the outdoors, which are easily accessible through the breakfast room.

Exterior:
(*Front*) The covered porch with columns and a dormer above lend drama to this impressive two-story home.

Photographed home may have been modified from the original construction documents.

Rear Elevation

Frank Betz Associates, Inc.

CHPFB01-853
1-888-840-6020

Bedrooms:	4
Bath:	3-1/2
Width:	54'0"
Depth:	43'4"
1st Floor:	1415 sq ft
2nd Floor:	1015 sq ft
Living Area:	2430 sq ft
Foundation:	Crawl Space or Basement
Price Code:	G

© 1995 Frank Betz Associates, Inc.

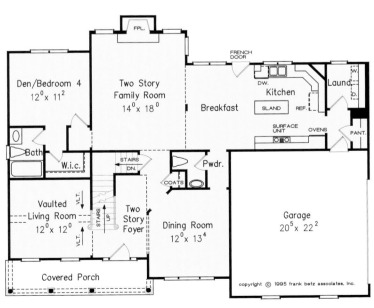

First Floor

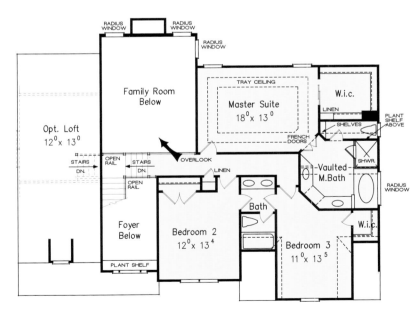

Second Floor

© 2003 Frank Betz Associates, Inc.

This home is every bit as quaint as its name, with a cedar shake exterior accented with a rooftop cupola. A seated shower, soaking tub and his-and-her closets make the master bath feel like five-star luxury. Optional bonus space upstairs leaves room to grow, making an ideal playroom or fifth bedroom.

Tullamore Square
Frank Betz Associates, Inc.
CHPFB01-3801
1-888-840-6020

Bedrooms:	4
Bath:	3
Width:	55'0"
Depth:	48'0"
1st Floor:	1805 sq ft
2nd Floor:	593 sq ft
Living Area:	2398 sq ft
Bonus Room:	255 sq ft
Foundation:	Slab, Crawl Space or Basement
Price Code:	H

Rear Elevation

First Floor

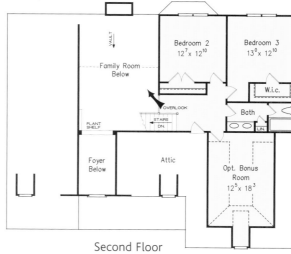

Second Floor

© The Sater Design Collection, Inc.

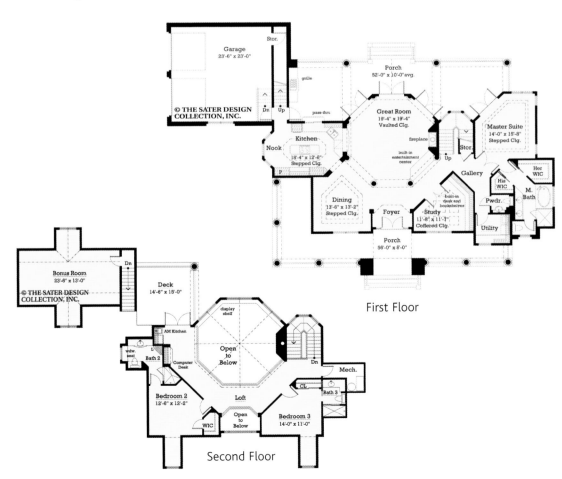

First Floor

Second Floor

The octagonal-shaped great room boasts three double French doors to the rear porch, a built-in entertainment center and fireplace. A bay-window kitchen provides easy access to formal and casual dining areas as well as the great room. The master suite features his-and-her walk-in closets, a spacious bath and opens onto the rear porch through French doors.

Newberry
The Sater Design Collection, Inc.
CHPDS01-7059
1-888-840-6020

Bedrooms:	3
Bath:	3-1/2
Width:	90'6"
Depth:	61'0"
1st Floor:	1995 sq ft
2nd Floor:	948 sq ft
Living Area:	2943 sq ft
Bonus Room:	371 sq ft
Foundation:	Crawl Space or Opt. Basement
Price Code:	G

Rear Elevation

PINEBROOK
frank betz associates, inc.

The sizeable square footage of the *Pinebrook* allows for extra design features that so many enjoy today. Inside, columns define the dining room that, along with the living room, flanks the foyer. Beyond the foyer is the great room, which boasts a 13' ceiling. French doors and a fireplace provide additional luxury and custom features to the great room.

A large breakfast area with tray ceiling is situated off the kitchen, featuring a wall of windows that overlooks the backyard. Enjoying a wing of its own, the master suite incorporates a sitting room that provides space and ensures relaxation. Built-in shelves, dual sinks, a separate tub and shower make the master bath a place for rejuvenation.

On the other side of the home are two secondary bedrooms, which share a bath with dual sinks. Upstairs, an optional bonus room, bath and walk-in closet are available. As an ideal teen suite, guest room, playroom or an exercise space, the bonus room is filled with flexibility.

Above:
By choosing to add a basement level, this homeowner created an ideal recreation space.
Right:
A perfect blend of rustic charm and stylish features make this great room truly remarkable.

Craftsman's Corner

Square columns are a defining Craftsman feature on this charming cottage.

Above:
The stone fireplace and bar exudes warmth and a sense of family.

Right:
Carrying the stacked stone into the kitchen gives the home the feeling of continuity.

Exterior:
(Front) A triplet of dormers and arched entryway say welcome to any passersby.

Rear Elevation

Frank Betz Associates, Inc.

CHPFB01-1158
1-888-840-6020

Bedrooms: 3
Bath: 3-1/2
Width: 61'0"
Depth: 58'6"
1st Floor: 2072 sq ft
Living Area: 2072 sq ft
Opt. 2nd Floor: 372 sq ft
Foundation: Slab, Crawl Space or Basement
Price Code: F

© 1998 Frank Betz Associates, Inc.

Opt. Second Floor

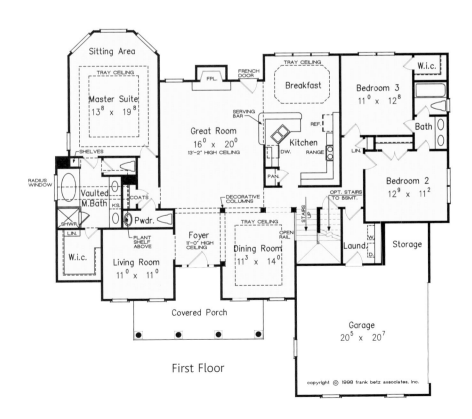

First Floor

© 2003 Frank Betz Associates, Inc.

The master suite enjoys the privacy of being the only bedroom on the main floor, and features a cozy window seat accented by decorative columns. A keeping room is situated next to the kitchen, making the ideal location for casual family time, as well as entertaining.

Hickory Grove

Frank Betz Associates, Inc.

CHPFB01-3800
1-888-840-6020

Bedrooms: 4
Bath: 3-1/2
Width: 54'0"
Depth: 63'6"
Main Level: 1977 sq ft
Lower Level: 940 sq ft
Living Area: 2917 sq ft
Opt. 2nd Floor: 260 sq ft
Foundation: Basement
Price Code: H

Rear Elevation

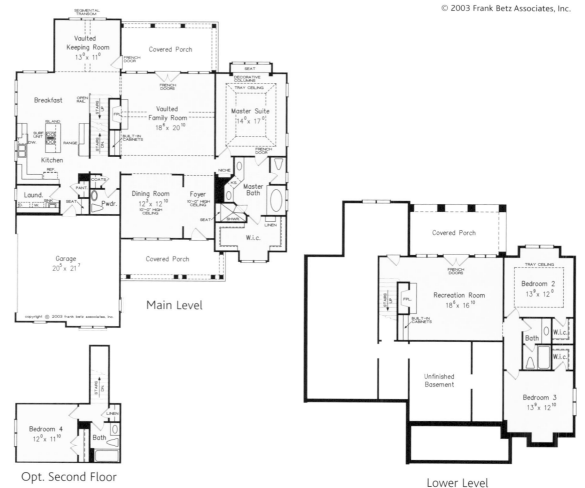

Main Level

Opt. Second Floor

Lower Level

© CornerStone Designs, LLC.

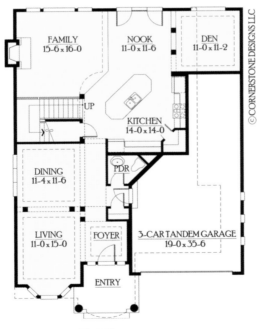

FAMILY
15-6 x 16-0

NOOK
11-0 x 11-6

DEN
11-0 x 11-2

UP

KITCHEN
14-0 x 14-0

DINING
11-4 x 11-6

PDR

LIVING
11-0 x 15-0

FOYER

3-CAR TANDEM GARAGE
19-0 x 35-6

ENTRY

First Floor

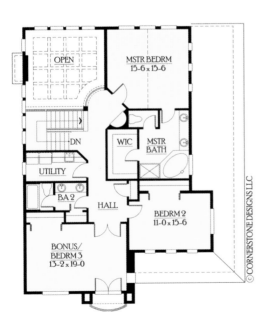

OPEN

MSTR BEDRM
15-6 x 15-6

DN

WIC

MSTR BATH

UTILITY

BA 2

HALL

BEDRM 2
11-0 x 15-6

BONUS/ BEDRM 3
13-2 x 19-0

Second Floor

Columns and shingles combine for a fresh look on this compact Hampton-style home. The Romeo-and-Juliet entry balcony, tower and cupola create a romantic, inviting image. The floor plan locates formal rooms at the front and a volume family living, dining, den and kitchen space towards the rear. Cased openings, columns and coffered ceilings highlight and define individual spaces.

Talus
CornerStone Designs
CHPCD01-M2520C3FT-0
1-888-840-6020

Bedrooms:	3
Bath:	2-1/2
Width:	41'6"
Depth:	54'8"
1st Floor:	1378 sq ft
2nd Floor:	1295 sq ft
Living Area:	2673 sq ft
Foundation:	Crawl Space
Price Code:	F

Rear Elevation

Fieldstone and cedar shake, accented by board-and-batten shutters, create the ideal cottage façade. A study is located just off the foyer, making the perfect home office. The master suite earns its name with a sitting area, luxurious bath and corner soaking tub.

Windward

Frank Betz Associates, Inc.

CHPFB01-3652

1-888-840-6020

Bedrooms:	4
Bath:	2-1/2
Width:	55'0"
Depth:	54'0"
1st Floor:	1969 sq ft
2nd Floor:	894 sq ft
Living Area:	2863 sq ft
Bonus Room:	213 sq ft
Foundation:	Crawl Space or Basement
Price Code:	I

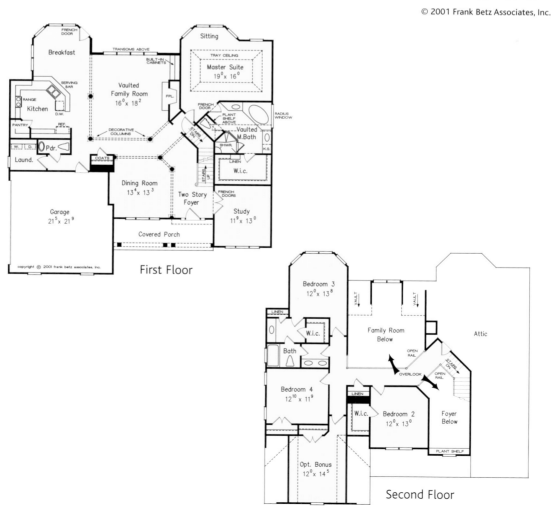

First Floor

Second Floor

Rear Elevation

The eye-catching exterior of the *Delaney* draws attention to three graceful arches across the front of the home. The classic incorporation of brick and dormers creates a timeless façade. Traffic flows easily from the kitchen area into the great room, creating functional space for entertaining. The study easily converts into a fourth bedroom for larger families or overnight guests.

Delaney
Frank Betz Associates, Inc.
CHPFB01-3744
1-888-840-6020

Bedrooms:	4
Bath:	4
Width:	60'0"
Depth:	47'6"
1st Floor:	1996 sq ft
Living Area:	1996 sq ft
Opt. 2nd Floor:	258 sq ft
Foundation:	Crawl Space or Basement
Price Code:	G

Opt. Second Floor

First Floor

Rear Elevation

SUMMERFIELD
frank betz associates, inc.

With subtle arches that add architectural interest to the porch's clean-lined roof and columns, this home is an attention-grabber. A perfectly placed arch frames the arched transom of the dining room window, allowing more light to enter the home. Other thoughtful touches are evident throughout the floor plan. Columns are utilized as accents throughout the first floor, and a plant shelf provides a perfect spot for showcasing collectibles in the vaulted keeping room. In the master suite, columns frame a generous sitting area to allow Mom and Dad private space for relaxing. Upstairs, the secondary bedrooms enjoy ample bathroom space and easy attic access for extra storage. The large utility room makes laundry day less of a chore for the entire family.

Above Right:
The great room features a centrally located fireplace and vibrant wall color to create the ultimate entertaining space.

Right:
The vaulted keeping room includes a second fireplace and built-in shelves and cabinetry for showcasing knick-knacks and family photos.

Exterior:
(Front) Arched keystones mimic the arched entryway, while various gable pitches and mixed materials enhance the exterior.

Rear Elevation

Frank Betz Associates, Inc.

CHPFB01-3550
1-888-840-6020

Bedrooms:	3
Bath:	2-1/2
Width:	58'4"
Depth:	55'2"
1st Floor:	2087 sq ft
2nd Floor:	593 sq ft
Living Area:	2680 sq ft
Bonus Room:	249 sq ft
Foundation:	Crawl Space or Basement
Price Code:	G

Photographed home may have been modified from the original construction documents.

First Floor

Second Floor

© 2002 Frank Betz Associates, Inc.

Copper window accents, brick and an arched, covered entry come together to create a warm *Brookhollow* welcome for family and guests. The main living area is airy and unobtrusive, with decorative columns serving as the subtle border of the dining room. Radius windows on each side of the fireplace allow natural light to pour into this living space.

Brookhollow

Frank Betz Associates, Inc.

CHPFB01-3694
1-888-840-6020

Bedrooms:	3
Bath:	2
Width:	54'0"
Depth:	59'6"
1st Floor:	1768 sq ft
Living Area:	1768 sq ft
Opt. 2nd Floor:	354 sq ft
Foundation:	Slab, Crawl Space or Basement
Price Code:	F

Opt. Basement
Stair Location

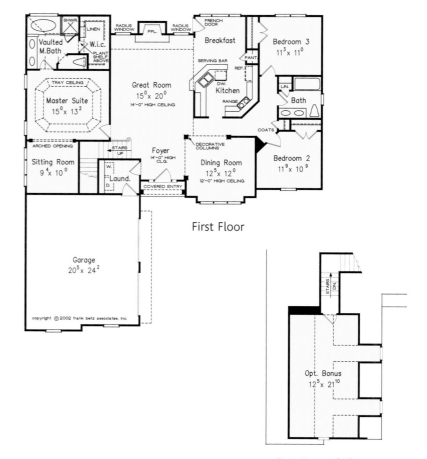

First Floor

Opt. Second Floor

Rear Elevation

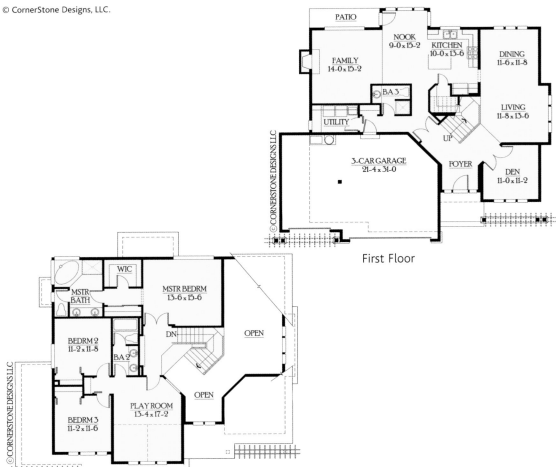

First Floor

Second Floor

Romantic trellises embrace the façade of this Craftsman charmer. The flared stair combines with vaulted and coffered ceilings to create a dramatic, sculptural feel. The versatile floor plan is designed for today's lifestyle, with the work-at-home den located at the entry. Upstairs is a grand master suite and a two-bedroom children's suite with bath and playroom.

Trelliswood
CornerStone Designs
CHPCD01-M2490B3F-0
1-888-840-6020

Bedrooms:	3
Bath:	3
Width:	52'0"
Depth:	48'0"
1st Floor:	1364 sq ft
2nd Floor:	1148 sq ft
Living Area:	2516 sq ft
Foundation:	Crawl Space
Price Code:	F

Rear Elevation

LONGLEAF
frank betz associates, inc.

A number of features make this home extraordinary – from three garage bays with close proximity to the kitchen to the remarkable coffered ceiling that distinguishes the family room. Notice the careful placement of the kitchen sink that allows for a clear line of sight through the family room all the way to the foyer. Built-in shelves near the dining area are placed to be easily viewed from the adjacent family room as well. The second floor offers as much attention to detail as the first, with walk-in closets in two of the three secondary bedrooms and a spacious room dedicated to family entertainment. The master suite includes a sophisticated tray ceiling, a large sitting room, a window seat overlooking the back yard, and a dream of a master bath.

Above Right:
The unique ceiling treatment makes this master one of a kind.
Right:
A stone archway and fireplace become striking focal points in the family room, while the coffered ceiling lends drama.
Exterior:
(Front) The metal roof and friendly portico blend to create a striking façade.

Rear Elevation

Frank Betz Associates, Inc.

CHPFB01-3782
1-888-840-6020

Bedrooms:	5
Bath:	4-1/2
Width:	69'0"
Depth:	54'4"
1st Floor:	1773 sq ft
2nd Floor:	2293 sq ft
Living Area:	4066 sq ft
Foundation:	Crawl Space or Basement
Price Code:	J

© 2003 Frank Betz Associates, Inc.

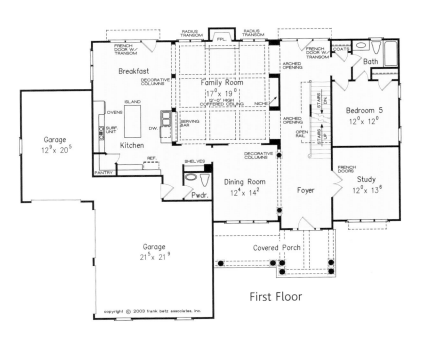

First Floor

copyright © 2003 frank betz associates, inc.

Second Floor

© 2002 Frank Betz Associates, Inc.

Simply elegant outside and in, the *Bentridge* is well planned and functional. The main floor is dedicated solely to living space, while four bedrooms share the upper level. Ornamental columns and knee walls offset the family room, seperating it from the breakfast area, yet allowing for easy transition from one spot the the next.

Bentridge

Frank Betz Associates, Inc.

CHPFB01-3666

1-888-840-6020

Bedrooms:	4
Bath:	2-1/2
Width:	41'0"
Depth:	39'4"
1st Floor:	947 sq ft
2nd Floor:	981 sq ft
Living Area:	1928 sq ft
Foundation:	Slab, Crawl Space or Basement
Price Code:	G

First Floor

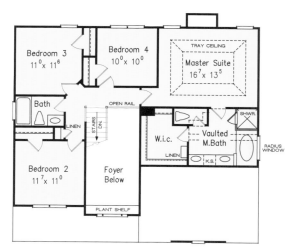

Second Floor

Rear Elevation

© 2002 Frank Betz Associates, Inc.

First Floor

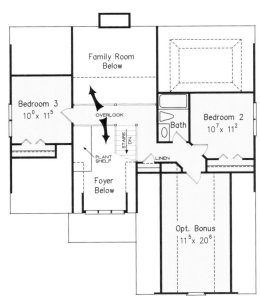

Second Floor

Brick and stone set off by multi-paned windows highlight the home. A sheltered entry leads to a two-story foyer and wide interior vistas that extend to the back property. Rooms in the public zone are open, allowing the spaces to flex for planned events. The vaulted family room frames a fireplace with tall windows that bring in natural light.

Brentwood
Frank Betz Associates, Inc.
CHPFB01-3711
1-888-840-6020

Bedrooms:	3
Bath:	2-1/2
Width:	41'0"
Depth:	48'4"
1st Floor:	1177 sq ft
2nd Floor:	457 sq ft
Living Area:	1634 sq ft
Bonus Room:	249 sq ft
Foundation:	Crawl Space or Basement
Price Code:	F

Rear Elevation

ASTORIA
cornerstone designs, llc

A sculptural façade and expansive verandas create an image of comfort and warm welcome as you approach the *Astoria*. A dramatic 80-foot view axis through the rotunda to the family room fireplace greets you on entry. The convenient circular floor plan provides easy access to the den and formal living room, while connecting the kitchen and formal dining via the butlery. The covered outdoor dining and BBQ porch connect the family living areas to the outdoors.

The rotunda's circular stair leads you to the spacious master suite retreat. A guest suite, two children's suites sharing the turreted play loft, and a large media room with popcorn kitchen complete the upper floor.

Above Right:
The grand octagonal rear porch is an inviting place to relax. Luxurious columns, arches, and a traditional beaded ceiling highlight the fireplace, BBQ and skylights, making a delightful link to the lavishly landscaped back yard.

Right:
A soaring stone fireplace anchors the two-story family room, accented by a massive timber mantel and flanked by a built-in entertainment center. Banks of wood-trimmed multi-paned windows fill the space with light, while hardwood floors add warmth.

Exteriors:
(Front) Set against elegant shingle and stone gables atop a grand rounded front porch, the *Astoria's* dramatic white-trimmed turret is its most distinctive feature. Columns, shutters and varied window shapes add Victorian accents to a craftsman theme.
(Rear) Grand banks of windows grace the *Astoria*, flooding the interior with light while connecting its occupants with the outdoors. Porches, gables and bays create the strong composition from the rear.

© CornerStone Designs, LLC

Rear Elevation

CornerStone Designs, LLC

CHPCD01-M4725A4S-1
1-888-840-6020

Bedrooms:	4
Bath:	4-1/2
Width:	71'0"
Depth:	92'0"
1st Floor:	2375 sq ft
2nd Floor:	2875 sq ft
Living Area:	5250 sq ft
Foundation:	Crawl Space
Price Code:	J

Photographed home may have been modified from the original construction documents.

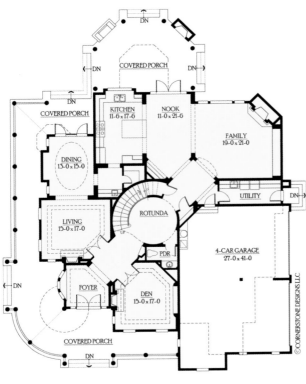

First Floor

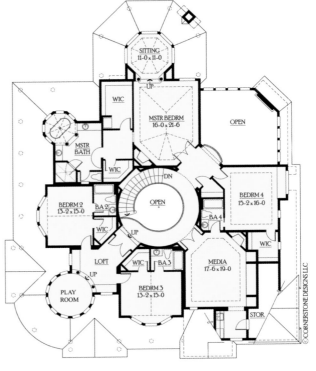

Second Floor

A striking blend of exterior materials gives this home a façade that radiates curb appeal. Built-in shelves, a fireplace and cathedral ceiling all accent the great room and showcase architectural detail. When enjoying Mother Nature, the rear porch can be accessed via the great room and also features skylights for natural illumination.

Raefield

Donald A. Gardner Architects, Inc.
CHPDG01-1123
1-888-840-6020

Bedrooms: 4
Bath: 2
Width: 63'8"
Depth: 63'8"
1st Floor: 2048 sq ft
Total Living: 2048 sq ft
Bonus Room: 476 sq ft
Foundation: Crawl Space*
Price Code: E

*Other options available. See page 175.

Rear Elevation

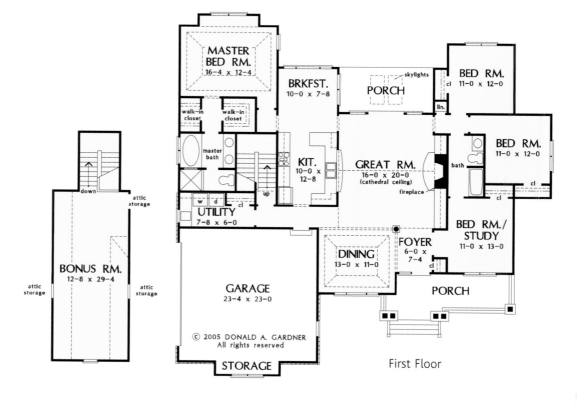

BONUS RM.
12-8 x 29-4

MASTER BED RM.
16-4 x 12-4

BRKFST.
10-0 x 7-8

PORCH

skylights

BED RM.
11-0 x 12-0

walk-in closet

walk-in closet

master bath

KIT.
10-0 x 12-8

GREAT RM.
16-0 x 20-0
(cathedral ceiling)

bath

BED RM.
11-0 x 12-0

fireplace

UTILITY
7-8 x 6-0

FOYER
6-0 x 7-4

BED RM./ STUDY
11-0 x 13-0

DINING
13-0 x 11-0

GARAGE
23-4 x 23-0

PORCH

STORAGE

First Floor

Step inside to find exceptional floor planning and details. A unique niche is incorporated into the foyer, providing the ideal location for that special furniture piece. Transom windows allow extra light to pour into the family room and a generously sized optional bonus area provides an additional bedroom, home office or exercise room.

Palmdale
Frank Betz Associates, Inc.
CHPFB01-3776
1-888-840-6020

Bedrooms:	4
Bath:	3-1/2
Width:	59'0"
Depth:	57'0"
1st Floor:	2073 sq ft
Opt. 2nd Floor:	350 sq ft
Living Area:	2073 sq ft
Foundation:	Crawl Space or Basement
Price Code:	G

Opt. Second Floor

First Floor

Rear Elevation

Quick Turnaround

Because you are placing your order directly, we can ship plans to you quickly. If your order is placed before noon EST, we can usually have your plans to you the next business day. Some restrictions may apply. We cannot ship to a post office box; please provide a physical street address.

Our Exchange policy

Since our blueprints are printed especially for you at the time you place your order, we cannot accept any returns. If, for some reason, you find that the plan that you purchased does not meet your needs, then you may exchange that plan for another plan in our collection. We allow you sixty days from the time of purchase to make an exchange. At the time of the exchange, you will be charged a processing fee of 20% of the total amount of the original order, plus the difference in price between the plans (if applicable) and the cost to ship the new plans to you. Vellums cannot be exchanged. All sets must be approved and authorization given before the exchange can take place. Please call our customer service department if you have any questions.

Local building codes and zoning requirements

Our plans are designed to meet or exceed national building standards. Because of the great differences in geography and climate, each state, county and municipality has its own building codes and zoning requirements. Your plan may need to be modified to comply with local requirements regarding snow loads, energy codes, soil and seismic conditions and a wide range of other matters. Prior to using plans ordered from us, we strongly advise that you consult a local building official.

Architecture and Engineering Seal

Some cities and states are now requiring that a licensed architect or engineer review and approve any set of building documents prior to construction. This is due to concerns over energy cost, safety, structural integrity and other factors. Prior to applying for a building permit or the start of actual construction, we strongly advise that you consult your local building official who can tell you if such a review is required.

Disclaimer

We have put substantial care and effort into the creation of our blueprints. We authorize the use of our blueprints on the express condition that you strictly comply with all local building codes, zoning requirements and other applicable laws, regulations and ordinances. However, because we cannot provide on-site consultation, supervision or control over actual construction, and because of the great variance in local building requirements, building practices and soil, seismic, weather and other conditions, WE CANNOT MAKE ANY WARRANTY, EXPRESS OR IMPLIED, WITH RESPECT TO THE CONTENT OR USE OF OUR BLUEPRINTS OR VELLUMS, INCLUDING BUT NOT LIMITED TO ANY WARRANTY OF MERCHANTABILITY OR OF FITNESS FOR A PARTICULAR PURPOSE. Please Note: Floor plans in this book are not construction documents and are subject to change. Renderings are artist's concept only.

How many sets of prints will you need?

We offer a single set of prints so that you can study and plan your dream home in detail. However, you cannot build from this package. One set of blueprints is marked "NOT FOR CONSTRUCTION." If you are planning to obtain estimates from a contractor or subcontractor, or if you are planning to build immediately, you will need more sets. Because additional sets are less expensive, make sure you order enough to satisfy all your requirements. Sometimes changes are needed to a plan; in that case, we offer vellums that are reproducible and erasable so changes can be made directly to the plans. Vellums are the only set that can be reproduced; it is illegal to copy blueprints. The checklist below will help you determine how many sets are needed.

PLAN CHECKLIST

_____ **Owner** (one for notes, one for file)

_____ **Builder** (generally requires at least three sets; one as a legal document, one for inspections and at least one to give subcontractors)

_____ **Local Building Department** (often requires two sets)

_____ **Mortgage Lender** (usually one set for a conventional loan; three sets for FHA or VA loans)

_____ **Total Number of Sets**

IGNORING COPYRIGHT LAWS CAN BE A

$1,000,000 mistake!

Recent changes in the US copyright laws allow for statutory penalties of up to $150,000 per incident for copyright infringement involving any of the copyrighted plans found in this publication. The law can be confusing. So, for your own protection, take the time to understand what you cannot do when it comes to home plans.

WHAT YOU CAN'T DO!

YOU CANNOT DUPLICATE HOME PLANS
YOU CANNOT COPY ANY PART OF A HOME PLAN TO CREAT ANOTHER.
YOU CANNOT BUILD A HOME WITHOUT BUYING A BLUEPRINT OR LICENSE.

1-866-525-9374

Select the option that corresponds to the designer of your home plan:

Frank Betz Associates, dial 01

Donald A. Gardner Architects, dial 02

Sater Design Collection, dial 03

CornerStone Designs, 12

This puts you in DIRECT contact
with the designer's office!

ADDITIONAL ITEMS**

Additional Sets (per set) $60.00

Full Reverse Set* $145.00

MATERIALS LIST*

Plan Categories A — E $75.00

Plan Categories F — O $80.00

FOUNDATION OPTIONS*
(basement, crawl space or slab, if different from base plan)
(no charge for Frank Betz plans)

Plan Categories A — C $225.00

Plan Categories D — E $250.00

Plan Categories F — M $275.00

Specification Outline* $15.00

*Call for availability. Special orders may require additional fees.

SHIPPING and Handling

Overnight .... $45.00   Ground $22.00

2nd Day .... $35.00   Saturday (if available) $55.00

For shipping international, please call for a quote.

**Products and prices vary for each designer.
Call for specific availability and pricing.

Plan Price Schedule*

	1 STUDY SET†	5 SETS	8 SETS	VELLUM	CD SETS†
A	$465	$535	$565	$710	$1420
B	$510	$580	$610	$775	$1550
C	$555	$625	$655	$840	$1680
D	$600	$675	$700	$905	$1810
E	$645	$720	$745	$970	$1940
F	$690	$765	$790	$1035	$2070
G	$760	$835	$860	$1115	$2230
H	$835	$910	$935	$1195	$2390
I	$935	$1010	$1035	$1295	$2590
J	$1035	$1110	$1135	$1395	$2790
K	$1135	$1210	$1235	$1495	$2990
L	$1235	$1310	$1335	$1595	$3190
M	$1335	$1410	$1435	$1695	$3390
N	$1435	$1510	$1535	$1795	$3590
O	Call for pricing				

* Prices subject to change without notice
† Call for specific availability.

Order Form

Plan Number _____

☐ 1-set [study only] .... $_____

☐ 5-set building package .... $_____

☐ 8-set building package .... $_____

☐ 1-set of reproducible vellums .... $_____

____ Additional Identical Blueprints @ $60 each $_____

____ Full Reverse Set @ $145 fee $_____

Foundation Options:

____ Crawl Space ____ Slab ____ Basement $_____
(no charge for Frank Betz plans)

Sub-Total $_____

Shipping and Handling $_____

Sales Tax *(will be determined upon placing order)* $_____

Total $_____

PLAN INDEX